WHERE IS EVERYBODY?

The Search for
Extraterrestrial Intelligence

Edward Ashpole

Published by Sigma Press, 1 South Oak Lane, Wilmslow, Cheshire SK9 6AR, England.

British Library Cataloguing in Publication Data
A CIP record for this book is available from the British Library.

ISBN: 1-85058-576-8

Typesetting and Design by: Sigma Press, Wilmslow, Cheshire.

Cover Design: MFP Design & Print

Cover Photograph: Beta Pictoris, one of the stars detected by the IRAS satellite in 1983 from its excessive emission of infra-red radiation. A disc of matter orbits the star and is twenty times the diameter of the solar system.

Printed by: MFP Design & Print

Preface

The search for extraterrestrial intelligence (SETI is the term used) may be a fringe science, but the question it seeks to answer is at the centre of human thought and imagination. SETI seeks to discover if life and intelligence are universal phenomena. And those who are currently trying to answer this question carry out scientific searches for evidence of life and intelligence beyond the Earth.

Since 1989, when this book was first published, scientists have made various discoveries directly relevant to SETI. These have inevitably changed our thinking about life and intelligence beyond the Earth, but the process of thinking about what information we already possess has also opened up SETI in several unexpected ways. I have therefore found myself rewriting most of the book for the second edition. There are many new sections, and few pages have been left unchanged. Astronomical SETI has increased phenomenally in its capacity to detect signals from other world civilizations, but developments outside the astronomical field are beginning to make us consider other ways of applying science to find evidence.

My view is that we are justified in assuming more latitude in SETI than could be tolerated elsewhere in science, because what is being tested is the most important hypothesis of all time. We can afford to be unconventional, as long as there's scientific rigour in our thinking and research. I think the reader will see from this book, which covers all the new and relevant scientific discoveries, that SETI is becoming increasingly fascinating and exciting.

The discovery of simple life-forms elsewhere in the Solar System is not main-line SETI, but it would provide encouraging support for SETI, and could revolutionize our understanding of life. The reader will therefore find that I have reviewed those scientific discoveries of the past few years which have drastically increased the possibility that life might thrive in certain environmental niches within the Solar System. Our current knowledge is sufficient to justify some highly sophisticated spacecraft to search for life deep beneath the Martian surface, and in the warm water which is thought to exist under the thick ice shell of Jupiter's moon, Europa.

Although on the scientific fringe – and, in some SETI research, just outside the fringe – there is no better subject than SETI (whether we find ET or not) for anyone who wishes to view the human situation against the best information and thinking that science can currently provide. I wanted to show in this book that the scientific rationale for astronomical SETI equally well supports the hypothesis that evidence of ET – and such evidence could be a few hundred million years old – may be discovered within the Solar System. It is self-evident, from what we know at present, that if it were possible for the ETs of our galaxy to have visited the Solar System, they would have done so. Our space scientists often publish articles on our future plans to explore the planetary systems of neighbouring stars. All we need is the space technology to do so. Why should we, therefore, deny the possibility of interstellar explorations to other civilizations which could have preceded us by millions of years? What would have stopped them from exploring and studying a planet so full of life as the Earth has been for the past 350 million years?

This is a point I have emphasised in the book because I believe this specific period of time is most significant for SETI. It is from about 350 million years ago that our atmosphere has been displaying the spectral lines of ozone and oxygen to any ET astronomers near enough to observe them. The prominent spectral line of ozone is most important because it would have told ET astronomers that they were looking towards a planet with abundant life. Consider what we would do in such a situation. Nothing would stop us from sending probes, if we had the space technology available and knew that an Earth-like planet was within an attainable distance – which we don't at present. Space scientists are already speculating about sending probes to other planetary systems within the next few decades. Therefore, if it's scientifically reasonable to think that we will send out intelligent probes on such missions, it must be even more reasonable to entertain the possibility that far older civilizations than ours have already done so.

In this book I have reviewed the few scientific hypotheses which could be tested to determine whether or not the Solar System has been visited. It's a side of SETI that is still almost unmentionable in scientific circles. Few scientists are in a position to venture beyond the fringe set by the science community. Also, astronomical SETI has made such progress in setting up research programmes to search for ET's broadcasts, and has gained so much deserved publicity, that it has dominated the field: other lines of investigation have, therefore, hardly been noticed. One would not wish to detract from astronomical SETI, which has been of major significance in science. Though actively supported by few scientists, it has focused the minds of a vast number of people on the most fundamental aspects of life and the universe. In this book, however, I have tried to show why astronomical SETI is no longer the only way to test the extraterrestrial hypothesis – which has been the case in SETI until recently. There are some other approaches, what we may call "local" approaches to the subject, which fully deserve our attention.

If, however, the ETs of our galaxy are either too far away to reach us, or if interstellar space cannot be crossed, then the astronomers have SETI all to themselves – and good luck to them. The problem is that we don't know if either of these conditions exists for highly advanced civilizations. For that reason we have to be prepared to test those hypotheses which could confirm that ET, or evidence of past ET activity, is within the Solar System.

I have, therefore, tried with this Second Edition to resist conventional wisdom and face up to possibilities which our current science shows us are probable. At present we do not know what the situation is out there, but we can obtain answers only by applying science. As the subject of SETI is on the fringe, it's going to be hard work making progress. Meanwhile, I hope a wide range of readers – non-scientists and scientists alike – will enjoy this book.

Edward Ashpole

Acknowledgements

So many people have provided information and counsel during the writing of this second edition that I cannot list all their names and affiliations. The list would be too long. They are mainly scientists at universities in Britain who work in astronomy, space technology and various areas of biology - and I thank them, every one. A new idea in SETI often involves obscure and highly specialised areas of science. This therefore necessitates finding appropriate members of the science community who may be able to comment on those areas of science. In the past nine months of my work on this book, I did not once encounter a scientist who was unwilling to be of assistance. That says much of the science community.

My thanks also to the staff at Sigma Press, especially to Graham Beech, the Editorial Director, whose contribution included obtaining essential new material from the Internet.

Contents

Chapter One

From Flash Gordon to SETI

My interest in life on other worlds goes back to the time when, as a boy, just before World War Two, I used to see Flash Gordon every Saturday morning at the local cinema. The simplicity of his space travel was far from the future reality. His visits to the planets were made on the spur of the moment. An old scientist, wide-eyed and clearly mad, had built a spaceship in his back garden and needed a crew. (In those days most scientists on the screen were old and mad.) So, off they went to save the world, or something equally grand, invariably accompanied by a glamorous female who was repeatedly rescued by Flash Gordon from the unwelcome attentions of sinister humanoid Martians and alien monsters.

The planets they visited (Mars was one of them) were populated by sharp-toothed prehistoric reptiles and bad actors indistinguishable from Homo sapiens. The Homo sapiens, divided into 'goodies' and 'baddies', fought one another with a strange mixture of weapons technology (swords and rayguns). Flash Gordon, unlike more conventional astronauts, was really good with a sword. And when the Homo Sapiens were not fighting one another, they were fighting the reptiles. They were great movies – for a small boy – and if the four pennies needed for a ticket could be obtained from my parents, I would not miss a Saturday morning at the local 'Plaza'.

More in touch with scientific reality in those pre-war days was a science magazine called "Modern Wonder", to which the boy next door sold me a subscription. The magazine had a healthy sprinkling of astronomy and science fiction among more mundane features, which I never read, on subjects such as how a telephone or an electric train worked. Somehow the insides of telephones and train engines never sparked my imagination in the same way as the Frogmen who lived on a tiny planet hidden permanently behind the Moon. You could hide anything behind the Moon at that time with no fear of being contradicted by NASA's next mission.

Among my fragmentary memories of "Modern Wonder" is an article, one of a series, on the shape of things to come. Its subject was 'When will men land on the Moon?', and its prediction (in 1938) was for 1968! Although only one year out in this prediction, it was a little wide of future reality in that it assumed trips to the Moon would soon become as commonplace as taking a plane from London to Paris. Yet it was not as far out as the scientists at a symposium in Washington in 1937 who concluded that we would never fly to the Moon. And even after the space age arrived, with the first satellites in orbit, the eleventh Astronomer Royal, Sir Richard Woolley, was describing manned space travel as 'bilge', which provoked a member of his staff to program the Observatory's computer to print out 'bilge' whenever its input was unsatisfactory. I remember one of the "Modern Wonder" illustrations which showed people queuing for the Moon Bus, and I did a little arithmetic on the kitchen table to see if I might still be around in 1968, not, perhaps, to join the queue, but to learn from others what it was like on the Moon.

The Moon has been tremendously important to our species. This sterile world has pulled us into space. The Moon was near enough to be a realistic challenge at the time when President Kennedy was looking for a venture to inspire the American people and impress the Soviet Union. The Moon is a perfect stepping-stone into the Solar System, and a civilization without a Moon might be far slower to launch itself into space.

Even in "Modern Wonder" days, however, the Moon was known to be a dead world. My interest in astronomy was largely stimulated by what 'old school' science fiction writers were interested in when they looked out into the universe – life on other worlds. Astronomy offered the only way to scientific knowledge of other worlds, and astronomers at that time offered in their popular books the only reasoned speculations published on life beyond the Earth. Biologists in that period didn't ever think about such things; thinking about life on Earth was enough for biologists, and for most people. Despite the work of Copernicus and his followers four centuries ago, the Earth for most of us still seemed the centre of the universe. No one guessed that within three decades science and technology would be examining the planets at close quarters, and searching for extraterrestrial life. One well-known astronomer, writing about Venus as late as 1957, the year of Sputnik One, said: 'What the surface of the planet may be like beneath its impenetrable muffler of vapour is a mystery which may perhaps never be solved.' Eighteen years later, the Soviet craft Venus 9 and 10 were sitting on the planet's stony landscape taking photographs. Later Soviet craft then took more photographs, and the Americans, using radar, have mapped the entire surface of Venus from orbiting spacecraft.

Although past contributions from astronomers about possible life on other planets have been both basic and indispensable, biologists are really in a better position to provide insight into the subject. Yet it is only in recent years that a few biologists have speculated about extraterrestrial life and the chances of technological beings evolving elsewhere. Consequently we have failed to appreciate fully the long series of fortuitous events which have produced just one advanced technological species on Earth. When we consider the immense time-scale of organic evolution and compare it with our very recent arrival as technological beings, the prospect of advanced extraterrestrial life and its technologies becomes somewhat awesome, even forbidding. We begin to wonder about how many different forms technological beings may take, and how far they may go in the evolution and development of their intellects. Communications may be far more difficult than we have previously supposed. We begin to wonder about the human position on the cosmic scale, and we conclude that we may be a long way down that scale – somewhere near the bottom, if not actually at the bottom. And looking out into the universe, at all those stars on a clear night, we begin to feel rather like Sir Fred Hoyle's 'perfectly good cod swimming off Yarmouth pier which haven't the faintest idea of what goes on in Yarmouth'.

Fortunately, this feeling has never inhibited science fiction writers. Has there ever been a human space traveller in fiction who worried about the cosmic status of his IQ? The prospect of being too primitive to qualify for contact with the inhabitants of Planet-X never entered the minds of the astronauts of fiction from Flash Gordon to StarTrek's Captain Kirk, or anyone else in that popular saga.

How long, then, might it be before we need face such an embarrassing problem, before we discover evidence of extraterrestrial intelligence and gain some idea of where we stand as a species? Maybe the truth will remain beyond our reach for many generations, until new levels of science and technology can reveal it to us. Maybe the truth is almost within our grasp. In this book we will consider a range of possible answers to our questions about life and intelligence beyond the Earth. The indirect scientific evidence is really convincing and the question certainly is, "Where is everybody?"

What SETI has to offer

Although our view of life and the universe goes far beyond that enjoyed by any previous generation, this fact is not always appreciated. An encounter I once had with a Russian space engineer suitably illustrates our disregard of the riches on offer. He was sitting amidst a display of Soviet spacecraft at a Soviet Exhibition in London, the first time that a full range of spacecraft from beyond the old "iron curtain" had been shown in Britain. "Has it been a successful exhibition?" I asked. He looked a little despondent. "The people here," he said, "are not interested in the universe and space travel. Here I am to answer questions, but what do they all ask? They ask me, 'Please can you tell me the way to the toilets?'."

Like that exhibition, this book looks at the universe and life and space travel, but in an attempt to answer the question: "Can we find evidence of intelligence beyond the Earth?" If we did, it would mean that life is a universal phenomenon and that we are just one emerging part in the great scheme of things. At present we can't be sure about this.

If the development of the universe (the formation of galaxies, the evolution of stars and planets and the origin of life) leads universally to high levels of intelligence and consciousness, then the universe must mean more to us than it would if all life on Earth was a freak. Would we want to be a freak of nature, the only technological species in the cosmos? For life and intelligence not to exist throughout the universe, for it not to be an integral part of the whole, would seem very odd, especially when we consider life's tenacity and endurance on the surface of our planet for 4 billion years. That life has survived the most dramatic disasters (climatic, geological and astronomical) says much about this most remarkable phenomenon.

However, to justify the searches for broadcasts from other worlds which orbit other stars like the Sun, or look for evidence of life of some kind within the Solar System, we have to consider a range of fundamental information. Here we find immediate value in thinking about the problems of searching for evidence of ET. The background information comes from just those aspects of science that make us most aware of the human situation in relation to the history of life and the universe. We have to scrutinize ourselves, our origins and development and behaviour, to guess if anything like us has evolved elsewhere. And we have to try to anticipate the possible behaviour of our counterparts elsewhere, as they explore space and transmit information across the Galaxy. Only by doing so can we hope to look in the most appropriate ways to detect evidence.

Many newspaper articles and books have been written about 'visitors from other worlds' who land in flying saucers. Those scientists in astronomical SETI try not to think of such an unsettling situation, but there are plenty of apparently credible reports from the military, the police and from civil and airline pilots, plus far more reports that are far from credible*. It is generally accepted by the best investigators of the UFO phenomena that most reports are cases of misidentification, hoaxes, natural phenomena or are psychologically induced. Too much nonsense has been published during the past few decades about humanoid aliens landing in flying saucers, having a brief chat with the local inhabitants and then zooming off at fantastic speed.

We will consider later why it is that humanoid aliens don't fit in with our understanding of evolutionary biology, which literally thousands of biologists in different disciplines have given to us. Those reported occupants of flying saucers would have to be from our biosphere to make any biological sense. Another point which discredits those claims of direct contact with ETs is that the ETs never have anything to tell us that we do not already know, which seems strange for beings able to cross the light-years. My view, therefore, is that while the most credible UFO reports deserve proper scientific investigation, the sensational alien astronauts are the modern equivalent of fairies at the bottom of the garden.

Angels and UFOnauts

Visitations have always been reported in terms of the culture and beliefs of the time. Admittedly, they can hardly be reported in any other way, but we have to be highly sceptical of such stories. The angels in biblical times used to arrive in 'chariots of fire' and UFOnauts – at least in those stories which we can't believe – have

---

* See "The UFO Phenomena" by Edward Ashpole (pub. Headline), which provides a scientific review of the subject.

technology which is near to that which we could soon possess, such as nuclear-powered spaceships.

The authors of popular accounts of visitors from other worlds have, however, neglected the science that relates to their subject. What we know about life and the universe often makes such stories at best highly suspect, or at worst complete nonsense. Nevertheless, we should use available science and technology to look more closely at those aspects of the UFO phenomena which are so strange that they defy explanation in terms of current science. So far, however, almost all the scientific progress in SETI has been made by the scientists in astronomical SETI and their supporters.

In astronomical SETI the shift to scientific respectability has been remarkable. In little more than a couple of decades, the search for our counterparts in the universe moved from one which only science fiction writers explored to a central subject in science itself. Nowadays astronomical SETI draws in eminent scientists from around the world to large international conferences. That's a great achievement for a science on the fringe. Now let's look in more detail at what currently makes SETI both fascinating and important.

Chapter Two

The Question

S ome friends of the great physicist Enrico Fermi were once trying to persuade him, so the story goes, that an abundance of life and technological civilizations must exist on an almost limitless number of other worlds. "OK," he said, "but where is everybody?" That was in 1943, and although much has happened since to make a convincing theoretical case for an abundance of life throughout the universe, we are still asking Fermi's question.

However, having the advantage of several decades of scientific progress, we are now able to offer possible answers, and technology is available (mainly in radio astronomy) to begin to check our answers. What was once only entertaining speculation has become firmly based in science and technology.

Fermi's question is tantalising. A mass of indirect evidence from widely different sources supports the probability that extraterrestrial life and civilizations do exist, yet no one has so far discovered any acceptable direct evidence. Not that we should expect such evidence so soon; the search will not be easy and has only just begun. Radio astronomers in the United States, Russia, Canada, France, Germany and Japan have set up more than fifty observational programmes in the past few decades, and the major programmes are still in progress. The astronomers have not yet found any intelligent signals, although there have been some exciting false alarms. No one can even guess when success might come. It could be at any time: within the next decade, a century hence or far in the future when giant telescopes will be operated in space, or on the other side of the Moon, shielded from the increasing radio noise of Earth.

To get the subject of SETI into perspective we have to examine the relevant science and try to guess the correct answer to our question about what ET will do in order to contact and explore other worlds. A simple story illustrates the kind of situation we are in. One night before World War 2, Winston Churchill was leaving the House of Commons after a long debate on an unresolved question. Clement Attlee, who told this story, watched the great statesman depart. "You know," said one of Attlee's colleagues, "Winston has ten answers to this question and one of them is right!" Current SETI (Search for Extraterrestrial Intelligence) is like that*. There are ten answers ready and one may be right, although we don't know which one. Perhaps we've not yet thought of all the possible answers, but we can only do our best with what we can think of at present and perhaps form a few hypotheses which can tested, remembering always that a hypothesis is only scientific if it can be tested.

Other Inhabited Worlds

The idea of the plurality of inhabited worlds is as old as ancient Hindu theology, but it has not always been a popular idea. In 1600, the philosopher Giordano Bruno was burned at the stake in Rome for persistently proclaiming it. Rudolf Thiel, an eminent historian of astronomy, calls Bruno, "The ecstatic herald of science, the man who thought through the Copernican system to its logical conclusion and first revealed its true grandeur." Perhaps more than anyone, Bruno developed the ideas that followed the work of Copernicus and which are so much part of our own universal view.

"Copernicus had banished the Earth from the centre of the universe," wrote Thiel. "Bruno now did the same for the Sun; intuitively he realized that the Sun was only a star, one among millions of other stars." The stars were no longer points of light on a fixed celestial sphere which enclosed the whole universe, but suns separated by great distances. The concept of infinity in space was born.

As in Bruno's day, people everywhere have usually seen themselves as the special creation of God or gods, and the existence of alien beings of equal rank, or higher, as unthinkable. Today, without an opinion poll, it would be difficult to say whether this view of ourselves or the belief in a plurality of inhabited worlds holds ascendancy. However, although we can never prove that we are the

---

*When the possibility of using the apparatus of astronomy to detect evidence of extraterrestrial intelligence was first suggested, the term CETI (Communication with Extraterrestrial Intelligence) was coined. Very soon, however, the 'Communication' bit began to look over-ambitious and 'Search' was substituted.

special creation of God, the only sentient beings in the universe, we can test Bruno's belief in the plurality of inhabited worlds.

Although the tests are uncertain of success, there is a compensation. The relevant background information consists of fundamental science that relates directly to life and the universe and the human situation. Therefore, while we speculate about extraterrestrial life and alien intelligence we cannot help but look more closely at ourselves and what we are currently doing on this planet. Even if we fail to detect messages from the stars, the insight we can gain into our own position should be worthwhile.

Technology, Evolution and Habitation

When we try to estimate the average longevity of extraterrestrial civilizations (a major factor in estimating their abundance and, therefore, our chances of detecting their presence) we have to look at our own chances of survival. We find ourselves asking questions such as, "Is technology taking us to extinction or to a golden age?" and, "How might we develop technology to increase our chances of survival?" It is ironic that as we search for life beyond the Earth, the survival of our species has never been more in doubt, as high technology and the natural instincts of man look increasingly uneasy together.

But what is the probability that technological civilizations with a desire to communicate (like ourselves) have ever existed? To try and answer that question, we must consider how large a part chance has played in our being here; and also how much we look like a probable evolutionary development on a benign planet with a flourishing biosphere for about 4 billion years (see Fig. 2.1)

According to present-day biology, human beings (and all other species of animals and plants, bacteria and fungi) are the children of chance. We must be unique in the universe, say the evolutionary biologists, because of the incalculable number of chance events that have made us what we are. And that goes for every species of whatever kind on our planet. Yet, if we are looking for our counterparts with radio transmitters on other worlds, we can say that life and intelligence could be abundant in widely different forms. Those transmitters on Planet-X could be operated by octopoids with IQs well beyond anything a member of Mensa could offer.

Like the formation of galaxies, of stars within galaxies, of the heavy elements themselves which have been forged in the interiors of

THE QUESTION

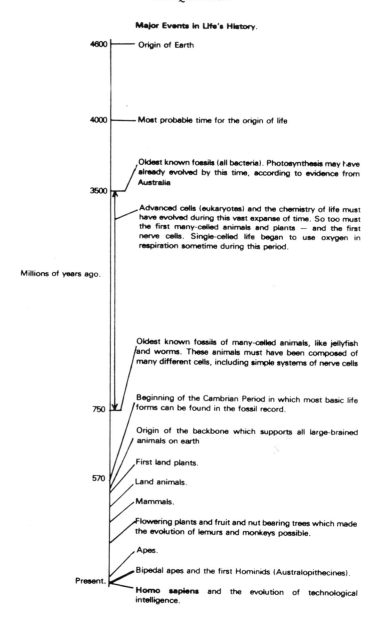

Major Events in Life's History.

4600 — Origin of Earth

4000 — Most probable time for the origin of life

Oldest known fossils (all bacteria). Photosynthesis may have already evolved by this time, according to evidence from Australia

3500

Advanced cells (eukaryotes) and the chemistry of life must have evolved during this vast expanse of time. So too must the first many-celled animals and plants — and the first nerve cells. Single-celled life began to use oxygen in respiration sometime during this period.

Millions of years ago.

Oldest known fossils of many-celled animals, like jellyfish and worms. These animals must have been composed of many different cells, including simple systems of nerve cells

750 — Beginning of the Cambrian Period in which most basic life forms can be found in the fossil record.

Origin of the backbone which supports all large-brained animals on earth

First land plants.

570

Land animals.

Mammals.

Flowering plants and fruit and nut bearing trees which made the evolution of lemurs and monkeys possible.

Apes.

Bipedal apes and the first Hominids (Australopithecines).

Present.

Homo sapiens and the evolution of technological intelligence.

Fig. 2.1

massive stars, the build-up in molecular complexity that led to life on Earth – all this appears to be inherent in the nature and forces of the universe and in the nature of matter. Given enough time, and the universe offers plenty of time, we can reasonably expect other technological creatures to evolve on other planets because there should be so many planets like the Earth. So-called "blue planets", because the Earth looks so blue from space, with abundant water and enough mass and, therefore, gravity to hold on to an oxygen and nitrogen atmosphere. But no matter how much such planets are like the Earth, no single life-form on any of them could be exactly the same as a species on Earth, and that includes our own species. The countless number of genetic steps which have made us what we are ensure that no one who has evolved on another planet could be mistaken for a member of *Homo sapiens*.

Thanks to Charles Darwin and several generations of evolutionary biologists, we see ourselves as a unique animal species among millions of other equally unique animal and plant species that have evolved on one favoured planet during the past four billion* years. But whether four billion years is a long or a short time for organic evolution to produce just one technological species we do not know, although theoretical research on the evolution of the Earth's atmosphere and the evolution of life is beginning to show why it has taken so long.

Habitable Zones

Mathematical and computer studies of the evolution of planetary atmospheres and the so-called habitable zones around stars indicate that life much beyond the microbial stage may be restricted to planets similar to the Earth, which orbit stars similar to the Sun. The physical conditions essential for the origin of life and its evolution into advanced forms seem to depend upon a planet having roughly the same mass as the Earth and an orbit within a limited zone. (We will consider this in more detail later.) The star (sun) of any continuously habitable planet may have a mass not greatly different from that of the Sun.

---

*Throughout this book 'billion' means a thousand million (1,000,000,000). This is the meaning of the word as adopted by science. It is a useful term where we have to use very large numbers, such as in astronomy and biology.

Some theoretical studies have indicated that the 'continuously habitable zone' in which the Earth has its orbit is more limited (narrower) than was previously assumed. According to Professor Michael Hart's work some years ago, the Earth's orbit only just comes within such a zone. Had the Earth been a few per cent closer to the Sun, it would have suffered a runaway greenhouse effect early in its history and become a furnace like Venus. Had it been a little further away from the Sun, it would have become a permanently frozen world like Mars. This is the result of a major, but only theoretical study. It's not established fact. It could be, however, that Earth-type planets may not be as abundant as we thought in the early days of astronomical SETI. We now begin to see some of the obstacles to such an abundance. Nevertheless, the question we must ask is, "Are there enough Earth-like planets to justify searches for signals from other civilizations?"

Here we meet an intriguing development of recent years. While astronomical research is showing that Earth-type planets may be rarer than we thought, other developments are showing that their abundance or otherwise may not be relevant to the abundance of civilizations in the Galaxy. The pioneering work of the late Gerard K. O'Neill, a professor of physics at Princeton University, and of his colleagues, has modified our thinking about the significance of habitable planets in SETI. O'Neill's pioneering work on the development of space stations and space colonies demonstrates the possible future potential of our space technology. The human race could have a fabulous future in space. Currently, however, one essential ingredient for that future is missing. We have no practical system of space propulsion which would enable us to go into space as easily as we cross the Atlantic in an airliner. My view is that we lack such a system because we don't yet know enough physics. When you look at science today, the knowledge we would need to develop a revolutionary means of space flight can come only from fundamental physics. Future knowledge may one day enable the human race to control the mass of spacecraft or generate powerful gravitational fields which would enable our spacecraft to fly as routinely as today's aircraft. Alternatively, it could be that Nature does not offer such knowledge for new technology. If that is so, then the real space age will never dawn. But if it does exist, then there is no reason to think that our future in space would be very different from that of other technological species which have evolved elsewhere in the Galaxy during past epochs.

We are, therefore, beginning to see that the forces and problems inherent in technological growth may have forced many ETs into space; that they may go into space in order to survive and not just to satisfy curiosity and the need for adventure. Yet, to do so, they would need a propulsion technology which is a quantum leap beyond anything we can currently develop, even in theory.

Exploration and Colonization

By taking a statistical view of ourselves, and this is the easiest and safest thing to do, we can assume that we are not the first technological species to evolve in the Galaxy*. The great age of the Galaxy (at least twice the age of the Sun) is all important when we speculate about the activities of advanced technological civilizations in past and present epochs (see Fig. 2.2). For widespread exploration and some colonization, it would be enough for stars like the Sun to have been forming just a billion years before the formation of the Solar System, and, according to the astronomical evidence, they were certainly doing so. It is, therefore, highly unlikely that we are the first creatures to spread space age wings. Many intelligent species could have done so already, and many more may do so when we and the Earth have returned to interstellar dust.

Since, therefore, ETs could have been crossing interstellar space to explore and colonize for the past few billion years, the Galaxy could be a hive of interstellar activity, which we couldn't expect to detect. A successful technological species might build its own habitats in space, so that just one intelligent species might establish a vast number of civilizations, providing its space technology was adequate. I cannot, however, imagine an advanced society crossing interstellar space to study a blue planet like the Earth and then going on to colonize it. That would mean destroying what they had crossed the light-years to explore, though we could speculate that ETs might set up home on, or in, lifeless real estate such as small moons and asteroids.

Yet the idea of super intelligent beings using up their lives travelling across the Galaxy does not seem credible. Robots with high artificial intelligence seem the most likely space travellers. They

---

*Throughout this book, I have written "Galaxy" with a capital letter to mean our Galaxy, part of which we see as the Milky Way. It is life in our Galaxy which we must first consider. Life probably exists in the billions of other galaxies in the universe, but we need not consider them at present.

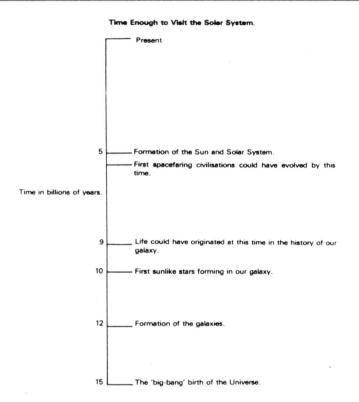

Fig. 2.2

could, perhaps, bring the 'blueprints' of their makers, the super-being genetic codes, so that copies of the 'home' species could be recreated anywhere in the Galaxy. The trouble with this scenario is that the time needed to cross the light-years might make the genetic code of the home species out of date. Maybe it would be more practical just to use robots who could continuously update their technology whenever they thought of desirable improvements.

One problem with SETI is that it is so easy to slip into science fiction. However, we can consider whether or not a state of colonization in the Galaxy would be inconsistent with our present lack of evidence of extraterrestrial intelligence. As the Solar System has been open to visitors for so long, some scientists have suggested that we may find probes, or the remains of them, which ETs sent long ago to study the Sun and its planets; or we might discover some totally unexpected evidence, such as alien artefacts on Mars. (See Chapter 11)

The main point for us is that there is no reason for ETs and their civilizations to be more in evidence today than at any other time in human history or prehistory. The search is on now only because we have become aware that detectable evidence of ETs may exist. We have run into an intriguing situation because of what we have discovered about life and the universe. There is a convincing theoretical case for the existence of ETs, but no acceptable scientific evidence has yet been obtained.

The Basic Question

Although we can today ask many specific questions about life and intelligence in the universe, Fermi's question, "Where is everybody?", remains the basic question. It confronts us with the greatest gap in human knowledge. We have the kind of anticipation that must have preceded the Copernican and Darwinian revolutions: a feeling for the truth without proof.

The revolution in thought which Copernicus started in the fifteenth century, when he showed that the Earth is just one planet of a planetary system orbiting the Sun, changed our relationship to the universe. The Darwinian revolution, while shattering the intellectual peace of nineteenth-century Christian thought, changed our relationship with the rest of life on Earth, and to God. We, who had remained aloof and distinctly separate as God's special creation, became a part of nature and went on to discover our origins in nature.

The discovery of a technological intelligence elsewhere in the universe would lead us into a revolution in thought and attitudes no less impressive than those precipitated by Copernicus and Darwin. Although we have been fed for years on science fiction, and are used to having science fiction turned into science fact, the reality of actually knowing that *they* are out there would shock in a way that Copernicus and Darwin never did. Our relationship to life and the universe would be changed yet again. More than anything else, our relationship to humankind itself would be changed. The knowledge that non-human minds, which could be superior in ways we cannot imagine, were out there beyond the Solar System could make us more conscious of our own nature and predicament. We might come, at last, to agree with H.G. Wells that our true nationality is the human race.

Chapter Three

Ceilings

ost of us look upon science as an unending source of
knowledge which will be used to develop more and more
advanced technologies. Science fiction writers especially
have helped to foster this view. If we don't destroy ourselves within
a century or so, the current image of the future is one overflowing
with technological marvels. We have been conditioned to think thus.
So far, in our technological infancy, new science and technologies
have crashed through the hypothetical barriers proclaimed by the
cautious and the pessimistic. The curiosity of scientists and the
inventiveness of technologists have been overwhelmingly trium-
phant. Consequently we have come to believe that this process will
go on for ever, that there are no barriers to stop our technological
advances. In time, almost everything will be possible.

Some years ago, Carl Sagan suggested that it might not be possible
to communicate with civilizations just a thousand years ahead of us
because the differences between what we are today and what we may
become in a thousand years of advancing science and technology
could be unbridgeable. The technologies of other world civilizations
could therefore appear to us as magic.

It could be that Sagan is right, if there is no ceiling to applicable
knowledge in our universe. An unending advance for technology may
be possible, though such an idea is impossible for the human mind
to grasp. For us there must be a limit to everything. Most astronomers
and physicists accept that current observations of the far regions of
space indicate that the universe is finite; and it would follow that the
information contained in a finite universe must also be finite. Thus,
it may be possible to possess all the information that would specify
the nature of matter and the laws and forces which determine its
behaviour. In other words, there may not be a limitless number of
layers of information to be peeled away as science proceeds. Thus, if

applicable knowledge is finite, there must be a ceiling to its applications, a ceiling beyond which no species can go regardless of how clever it may be. This line of thinking may seem very theoretical, but it is relevant to any SETI project. If the universal ceiling to knowledge about the universe is unimaginably high, then almost anything could be expected. If the ceiling is one which the human mind is capable of reaching within a century or so, then our expectations would be much more limited.

Let us accept for a moment that an unimaginably high ceiling to knowledge actually exists. This would then permit the great future advances of science and technology that in science fiction have so coloured our picture of extraterrestrial civilizations. Many extraterrestrial technologies would then surely appear to us as magic. On the time-scale of organic evolution, however, a thousand years is a mere instant. Therefore, if we could not communicate with ETs a thousand years or more in our future, then the number of civilizations with which we could communicate virtually disappears. All colonial ETs (those established in alien planetary systems though not necessarily colonizers of inhabited worlds), if such there be, would, of necessity, be at least thousands of years ahead of us. They would not have crossed the light-years and set up home in other planetary systems if they were not that far advanced.

For the astronomer in SETI, the situation where everyone stays at home and no one goes into the interstellar travel business is the best scenario. Next would be one where some interstellar exploration and colonization has been undertaken, but only locally on a small scale, leaving civilizations well spaced out, say thousands of light-years apart. The worst situation for the astronomers would be one where there exists a very high ceiling of knowledge, one which permits the development of interstellar transport that allows easy and rapid travel from star system to star system. Given this situation, ET could already be here in the Solar System. This situation would make the SETI astronomers redundant, though we would need plenty of scientists in various disciplines to search for evidence within the Solar System.

Limits to the Human Brain

Given our present rate of application to the task, it may be that the kind of fundamental knowledge of nature from which major new technologies can spring will be discovered within the next few centuries. In short, the scientific ceiling may be much lower than we have anticipated. Further discoveries are bound to be made, but not discoveries of a fundamental, applicable kind, like our knowledge of electricity and nuclear physics. Given that situation, the technologies of civilizations more than 1,000 years ahead of us, rather than appearing to us as magic, might be almost recognisable, with all technological ETs, except the very latest arrivals, applying the same science, the same knowledge, to reach the same 'levels of technical perfection' in their various technologies. They would reach the universal scientific and technological ceilings very early in their histories. In any case, given enough time, this situation seems inevitable for intelligent life, whether the ceilings are very low or so high that present human intelligence could never reach them. The state of affairs out there amongst the stars, however, would be very different for a low ceiling than it would be for a high ceiling to fundamental knowledge.

J.B.S. Haldane once said, "The universe may not only be queerer than we imagine, but queerer than we can imagine." We have only to consider how discoveries in astronomy have changed our view of the universe in the past 100 years to see that this is true in one sense. The universe that we know today is certainly 'queerer' than anyone could have imagined 100 years ago, but this is not what Haldane meant. He meant that the human brain may lack the capacity to comprehend the nature of the universe. In other words, the ceiling to complete understanding may be too high for us. There is, of course, no reason why we should expect to be able to comprehend the universe. We do not think it strange that the brain of a chimpanzee, our closest relative on Earth, cannot comprehend the universe, so why should we expect our brains to possess such an awesome capability? Our brains are three to four times larger than those of the most advanced apes, but a full understanding of the universe may need much more intelligence than any human brain can possess. Yet it does not follow that the universe will always be queerer than any level of intelligence can imagine, to use Haldane's words. Intelligence beyond our own may be capable of discovering all scientific knowledge, even if the ceiling is too high for us.

A great mystic and science fiction writer, Olaf Stapledon, wrote in the "Star Maker" in 1937, 'And this is the goal of all being, that the universe be known and admired and that it be bestowed with further beauties ...'. I copied Stapledon's words into a notebook some 35 years ago when I read "The Star Maker" and have since lost the notebook, so I'm relying on memory here and I may have slightly misquoted him, yet what he wrote encapsulated my feelings at the time and it still does.

So how far does intelligence have to advance before the universe can be known? Whether human intelligence can do so or not we cannot say, but we can say that a very low ceiling would determine a future on Earth distinctly different from that allowed by a very high ceiling.

Possible Futures

The purpose of our speculation is not to predict the future, but to try to find clues to what kinds of signs to look for in the search for extraterrestrial civilizations. It may also guide us in assessing the probability of there being any signs to search for. It seems that the future of humankind can go in only one of five ways:

1. Early extinction.

2. The breakdown of civilization and a return to permanent barbarism.

3. A cyclical future: barbarism – civilization – barbarism – civilization.

4. Scientific and technological advance to a low universal ceiling, or to a level beyond which the brains of Homo sapiens, or his descendants, cannot go, followed by a long period of consolidation and stability.

5. Continual scientific and technological advance to levels of civilization unimaginable to us and probably beyond the capacity of the present human brain to understand, as Haldane predicted. This future could involve a far more intelligent human species, perhaps a different being altogether, and highly advanced artificial intelligence.

It seems clear that the first three alternatives could be the future of any technological species, since technology brings biological success and over-population and opportunities to make increasingly effective weapons. Therefore, only the last two alternatives need concern us here. For all successful technological species – and it would apply to all – future 4 could explain why no one has completely colonized the Galaxy. No species has been able to muster the energy and technology needed, and no one ever will.

Considering our rapid advances in science and space technology, however, at least some interstellar exploration and colonization by other species seems inevitable. The occurrence of alternatives 1, 2 and 3 would clearly not contribute to colonization, although they could hardly be the fate of every world civilization. But given future 5 for just one technological species during the past few million years (plus the will to use unlimited science and technology to explore and expand its civilization) and the Gálaxy should have been colonized. Though this doesn't mean that planets like the Earth, the blue planets of the Galaxy, would be colonized, or that their intelligent inhabitants (if any) would see any evidence of such colonization. For reasons we will consider later, alien biospheres would be the least suitable places for ETs to colonize.

Alternatively, although a low scientific and technological ceiling (future 4) may take some of the thrill out of life for future scientists and technologists, it would have its compensations. No extraterrestrial civilization would be so far ahead of us that we might not eventually catch up. Interstellar communication by electromagnetic radiation (radio, light or another section of the electromagnetic spectrum) would be more likely to exist because the nature of the universe would probably not offer the basis for a better way. I mean that physics would not have to advance for a few more centuries before human beings discover the key to receiving messages from our intelligent neighbours in the Galaxy. Our self-esteem would also not be permanently crushed by knowing that we are no more than tenth-rate citizens of the Galaxy, or worse.

With very low ceilings, the cultural gap between ourselves and any ETs might be closed by Homo sapiens. Yet if ETs are many orders of magnitude beyond us in intelligence, and ceilings hardly exist, then it would be like trying to close the gap between ourselves and Sir Fred Hoyle's 'perfectly good cod off Yarmouth Pier that have no idea about what goes on in Yarmouth'.

For us, I think, the existence of very low scientific and technological ceilings would be best. It would be a more comfortable universe psychologically. The 'zoo hypothesis' (that the Earth is kept as a sort of planetary nature reserve, protected from the impact of advanced civilizations) is not one we would wish to be correct. We don't want to be inmates of a zoo, no matter how well-protected – though, of course, we don't mind putting our nearest primate relatives in zoos and using them for experimental purposes!

UFOs and Ceilings

Let us speculate freely here and provide support for the hypothesis that some UFOs are alien spacecraft. Let us say that the technological ceiling is high enough to make routine interstellar travel a feasible achievement. Now, although no scientifically acceptable evidence exists for flying saucers, this could explain the numerous consistencies in reports which describe them. In thousands of reports, including some from historical times, there are striking similarities in the appearance, size and behaviour of flying saucers. Perhaps not every witness has been soaked in UFO literature – at least the historical witnesses could not have been. So let speculation run free and say that these similarities in flying saucers exist because the optimum design and power system for space travel are soon developed, perhaps within a few centuries of our present technological state.

Are flying saucers, then, simply spacecraft at their level of technical perfectibility? We can imagine clever beings from different planets and of different biologies all applying the same limited knowledge of the universe and all ending up with spacecraft similar in form and function. It would be rather like the ways in which life on Earth has made the best use of the options open to it, so that quite independent and isolated groups of animals and plants have evolved similar forms and functions. Each has evolved a sort of 'technical perfectibility' for similar tasks and ways of life.

Biological Ceilings

This brings us to biological ceilings and to our examination of a biological ceiling to intelligence. Are beings with intellects several orders of magnitude superior to ourselves biologically probable or even possible?

Let's look at the evolution of the most advanced brains on Earth, those of the whales and dolphins and ourselves. We can see that where technology and civilization are not possible, there appears to be a ceiling to the evolution of brains. The whales and dolphins probably met their ceiling a few million years ago. For example, the ancestors of the bottlenose dolphin had already evolved their present advanced brains (as advanced in structure as ours and larger) a few million years ago, when our pre-human ancestors had brains no larger than those of present-day apes (see Figs. 3.1 and 3.2).

Living as they do in a natural environment, the whales and dol-

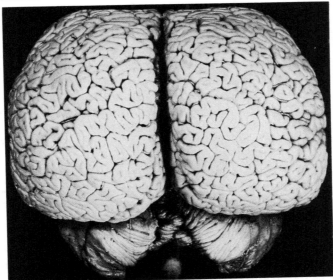

Fig 3.1: Brain of a bottle-nosed dolphin, weighing about 1700 g. With more convolutions than a human brain, it looks superior but has evolved mainly to process the range of sounds used in the dolphin's sonar system.

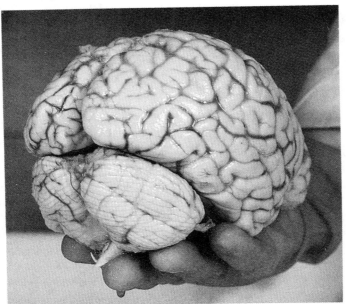

Fig 3.2: Human brains weigh 1000-2000 g but a heavy brain is no certain indication of high intelligence.

phins would have evolved even bigger brains and more intelligence had it been advantageous so to do, but they had all the brain power they needed for their way of life. Much of their spectacular brain development seems to be used to 'see' by sound in their underwater world. They seem to see by sound almost as well as we see by light, and such an ability requires a great deal of processing power.

Judging from the skulls of our ancestors, human brains reached a peak in brain size about 50,000 years ago, but it is not just a matter of brain size. During our evolution from ape to man, we must also have profited from advances in the brain's internal organization. For example, during evolution the two hemispheres of the primate brain became less like duplicates and were used increasingly for separate functions, thus speeding up the evolution of our ancestors.

A natural environment with hazards to human life that demanded much greater mental powers than we possess is hard to envisage, and it does not seem likely that intellects much greater than ours could evolve by natural selection. Unless more intelligence had survival value, it would not evolve. Could a slightly higher human intelligence have evolved had we not settled to agriculture and animal husbandry some 10,000 years ago? The answer from the human craniums of 50,000 years ago, which had on average a slightly larger capacity than today's craniums, is 'probably not'. In any case, as intelligence becomes greater the onset of civilization becomes more likely, and with it, as society develops, an end to further biological improvements by natural means.

The Way to Brighter Beings

We can see the way to brighter beings. I suppose it's something we might opt for in the future, once we've managed to obtain the best out of the neurological equipment which all the hardships of natural selection in the past have given us. It's something we couldn't choose now for obvious social and political reasons, but the increasing complexities of our civilization and technology could one day force us in that direction to cope with all the wonderful complexities that we have created. A ten per cent rise in intelligence with each generation would hardly be noticed. No one would mind having more intelligent offspring, providing they were only ten per cent brighter. Parents could cope with that differential. But after ten generations the average intelligence, as currently defined by the majority of psychologists, would be twice as great as it is now. Social life and international relations would be dramatically changed, hopefully for the better.

We cannot assume that the super brains possessed by some extra-terrestrial s in science fiction are natural products. If they exist in reality, they would have been bred artificially, or produced by biological engineering, or be electronic rather than biological brains. Whatever their nature and origin, the super brains would have needed beings like ourselves to take the first step towards producing them.

Would the human race, or biological ETs, take such steps? Our future generations may be forced to as the management of the world becomes more complex, although the move towards higher intellect could be made slowly. Doubling the intellectual capacity of mankind every 1,000 years might not cause social, psychological or personal problems, yet at the end of the period a new species of Homo would be controlling planet Earth. In this way, our overwhelming instinct for self-preservation would not stop our eventual replacement by a higher species of human being.

Nevertheless, there must be a limit to how far a species may go biologically in improving its brain by artificial means. We would be limited to improving what already exists in the human brain. We could not expect to evolve artificially a totally new neural structure, something not already existing in the human brain, which would give new and greater intellectual abilities. New neural structures with unimaginable functions could perhaps only come into being through millions of years of natural selection, and natural selection is a process in which most genetic changes perish when put on trial in the environment. New individuals, artificially produced, would have to be sound and healthy and an improvement, however slight, on the previous generation. The trial-and-error method of nature, where the errors are ruthlessly eliminated, could hardly be undertaken by a humane society. We would, therefore, be limited to improving what nature already provides. Another possible obstacle to 'super brains' concerns our DNA (deoxyribonucleic acid) which specifies everything we are, including the structures and functions of the brain. Conceivably it might not be adequate for 'super brain' plans, whatever they might be. A human intellect far beyond what we possess, with new capabilities, would have to be specified by our DNA, and it may not be biologically possible. The super brains, if they exist outside science fiction, may, therefore, have a basis other than protoplasm.

They may be electronic intelligences taken, no doubt, to their limit of technical perfectibility.

Future Electronic Beings

While we are speculating on a ceiling to brains and intelligence, we can hardly pass by questions often asked in science fiction: Would biological intelligence ever give way to electronic intelligence? Would we let the robots take over?

As already suggested, we might give way to a higher form of human being without defying our sense of self-preservation, providing it took place over a long enough period, say several dozen generations. We would never, however, willingly retire in favour of a machine. Although we cannot speak for a higher form of humanity, we can guess that it would no more give way to a society of bright robots than we would, for as we are (genetically) still mainly ape, so they would possess almost all our genetic code, with just a little extra that would make them superior. Likewise, all biological ETs, if they evolved by natural selection, would have self-preservation inexorably built into their genes. The super electronic brains would therefore be created to serve, and would take over only by mistakes on the part of their creators.

The biological ceiling for brains may therefore be low, and only the electronic brains that somehow escape from the control of biological brains may have the powers described in science fiction and, no doubt, a lot more besides. So, if anyone watches over the Galaxy, protecting us in a planetary zoo, it may be such artificial intelligences which, by this time in the history of the universe, may be forever beyond the understanding of biological beings.

It's not hard to accept that human brains, or the brains of beings elsewhere, may become more advanced through some form of directed breeding until the capacity and quality of intellectual life extends beyond anything we can imagine. And the robots, where they take over, could have even greater intellects. Nevertheless, their technological capabilities would still be limited, in the end, by the amount of applicable information in the universe.

Let us now turn to the probability that enough planets like the Earth have existed in the history of the Galaxy to have made advanced ETs and their civilizations possible.

Chapter Four

Planets for Intelligent Life

Thanks to the late Professor Gerard O'Neill's work on the feasibility of space colonies, we can see that ET civilizations may not be restricted to habitable planets. Indeed, for fundamental biological reasons, blue planets like the Earth, where life has evolved for billions of years, may be the most unsuitable places for any ET wishing to set up a new home. It may also be that blue planets are much rarer than we thought. It is beginning to look as if planets that are continuously habitable (continuously is the key word) can evolve only where a special set of conditions exist. Many planetary systems, which differ little from the Solar System, may not provide these conditions and, therefore, offer no cradle for the origin and evolution of advanced life-forms.

Yet ETs could, nevertheless, live in such planetary systems, secure in their own custom-built habitats which orbit stars that, for one reason or another, never sparked organic chemistry into life on any of their planets. Astronomers tell us that most stars are either too massive or not massive enough for the evolution of planets which remain habitable for several billion years. Planets like Earth may, therefore, be the rare places where technological civilizations are born, and not necessarily permanent homes for their long-term development. Moreover, lifeless worlds like the Moon, rather than being the sites of future civilizations, may be used as rich sources of materials to build space colonies. But for this kind of colonizing to have taken place, travel within planetary systems and amongst the stars must be a routine activity. We would need a new understanding of nature which could be applied to create the space technology to take us to the stars. The physicists may make the required discoveries in the decades ahead, or it could take centuries, but without that quantum lead in fundamental physics, which could lead to a new level in space propulsion, the real space age cannot begin. It's not encouraging, therefore, to note that leading politicians in the United States, which has led the world in science and technology, are cutting back on the research in particle physics which might lead, among other things, to an advanced system for space travel. I speak here, for example, of the giant particle accelerator that was being built in Texas until politicians decided to cancel it for economic reasons in 1995.

The point is that just to colonize its own planetary system, a successful technological civilization would need a propulsion system far superior to anything we could currently even begin to design. Think of the hundreds of flights that would be needed to begin to colonize our neighbour Mars, a relatively easy task compared to trying to colonize other planetary systems, the nearest of which is many thousands of times further away than Mars.

How many Blue Planets?

We know that our planet has evolved from the formation of an ordinary star, and that there are several billion stars like it in our Galaxy of more than a hundred billion stars. Thus, with billions of galaxies in the observable universe, there should be many planets like the Earth, even though only a small proportion of planetary systems may have one. The astronomers tell us that the formation of planets seems to be associated with the formation of at least a proportion of stars. Although planets are rather insignificant compared to stars (mere debris in a way) the fact that the *planetary system phenomenon* is repeated on a smaller scale within the Solar System suggests that this phenomenon may be widespread in the universe. Look at Jupiter and its fascinating worlds in orbit. Look also at the more distant gas giants Saturn, Uranus and Neptune and at their amazing satellites.

The gas giants may be little changed since their formation. Jupiter has been called a 'failed star' because of its great mass and similar composition to the Sun, although this planet needed to be fifty times more massive to have been the dimmest of red dwarf stars. This, apparently, is the minimum mass necessary to make a star. Otherwise there is not enough gravitational pressure to create the temperature needed to start the nuclear fusion of hydrogen.

In recent years some astronomers have suggested that the presence of Jupiter may have been essential for our presence here today. Planetary systems without such a massive planet, or planets, might not have planets with advanced life-forms for one simple reason. The fact is that space debris, including many massive bodies, bombarded the planets and moons within the Solar System during the first billion years of its formation. When we view the crater-scarred Moon and photographs of Mercury, Mars and many of the moons of the other planets, we can begin to appreciate how intense that bombardment was. The massive Jupiter and Saturn, with their powerful gravitational fields, must have soaked up a large proportion of the debris from the original solar disc. Had they not been present, this debris would have continued to orbit in space, constantly colliding with the Earth and other bodies of the solar system.

It's reckoned that a rock some ten miles across was enough to put an end to the dinosaurs 65 million years ago, and a vast number of other species at the same time. We have only to look at the largest craters on the Moon to see that the meteorite that hit the Earth 65 million years ago was small compared to the monsters that must have struck the Earth in its early days. If such large rocks had continued to hit the Earth throughout its history, the evolution of advanced land life would have been impossible. (see Figs. 4.1 and 4.2) Thus the presence of massive planets like Jupiter may be essential for the evolution of planets like the Earth.

A supernova some 6 billion years ago may also have contributed to the present existence of the Earth. (A supernova is a violently exploding star. Such a star, which has become unstable following the exhaustion of its nuclear fuel, will become, for a few days, up to 100 million times brighter than the Sun.) There is evidence that a supernova explosion increased the abundance of heavy elements in the gas cloud from which the Sun and planets formed. Astronomers think a supernova may have initiated the collapse of the cloud, as well as enriching it with heavy elements that can be synthesised only in such explosions. There is evidence for this in certain meteorites that contain material which is older than the Solar System by about a billion years.

Formation of Planets

Let us now take a brief look at the generally accepted theory of planetary formation. As the disc of gas around the primordial Sun cooled, the substances in it changed from gases to liquids to solids. These first steps in planetary formation have been worked out in theory with the help of meteorites.

First, metals and their compounds with a high boiling point coagu-

Fig. 4.1: Dr Dale A. Russell of the Canadian National Museum of Natural Sciences constructed this biologically credible creature to show how dinosaurs may have evolved had they not been brought to extinction by a massive meteorite which struck the Earth 65 million years ago.

Fig. 4.2: Dr Russell's reconstruction of *Stenonychosaurus*, seen here with its possible descendant, the intelligent dinosaur. The animal was about 2.5 metres from head to tail and a carnivore, judging from its teeth. What impressed Russell was the reptile's relatively large cranium, which suggested that *Stenonychosaurus* may have been as intelligent as a dull mammal.

lated into small spheres. Next, the silicates (elements combined with oxygen and silicon) condensed out, and so on. Not until temperatures within the gas fell to a few hundred degrees did the more volatile substances begin to condense. Clumps of matter then built up by collisions. Some clumps became very large and gathered more matter by gravitational attraction. It was a runaway process. All the planets and their moons show evidence of the last great bombardment by meteorites – debris from the primordial solar disc. The exceptions are the gas giants and the eroded face of Earth, plus those moons, such as Europa, which have renewed their surfaces in some way. Astronomers tell us that the great bombardment ended some 3.8 billion years ago; not that the bombardment has completely ended, of course, but these days we are not often hit by a large meteorite.

The planets which formed near the Sun by the condensation and coalition of matter, therefore, consist predominantly of the less volatile substances (metals and silicates). Those further out (the gas giants) formed mainly of the lighter elements. The inner planets, the rocky planets, did not, however, retain hydrogen and helium, although the primordial disc around the Sun must have been mainly composed of these two elements, the lightest and most abundant of all the elements. While the Sun's intense radiation drove these light gases from the inner planets, the gas giants retained hydrogen and helium by their high gravitational fields and low temperatures. It looks, therefore, as if rocky planets (like Mercury, Venus, Earth and Mars) and gas giants (like Jupiter, Saturn, Uranus and Neptune) may be inevitable products of the way in which stars and their planets form.

The Planets of other Suns

There is now evidence of six other planetary systems: six planets have been found to orbit six neighbouring stars like the Sun. A seventh planet has also been detected in the disc of dust and gas which orbits the star Beta Pictoris (see cover photograph) This disc is hardly a planetary system, though it might become one in time. These discoveries provide the first step in an area of astronomy which has suddenly begun to produce results after decades of patient research. The great significance of discovering the planets of neighbouring stars has driven astronomers towards perfecting their planet-hunting techniques. If the Solar System formed from an almost unique event, such as a near collision with another star soon after the Sun formed, as was at one time seriously suggested, then we could be on our own, even though a few billion stars in our galaxy alone are carbon copies of the Sun. Most astronomers have been inclined to reject the idea of the freak formation of the Solar System. When it comes to explaining reality, scientists don't like proposing freak events in their theories. They like explaining things in terms of processes. Given time, therefore, the planet searchers could show that the formation of planets is a common part of the great universal process from the formation of galaxies to the evolution of brains capable of creating the technology to discover other planets and other life.

We may have believed for years that those "strange new worlds" of "Star Trek" were out there, but the astronomers have had to prove it. Belief is not enough in science. Anyone who thinks that life should be a universal phenomenon needs indisputable evidence of potentially habitable planets beyond the Solar System Without such planets there can be no life and no intelligence elsewhere, though the detection of many planetary systems would not guarantee the presence of life, and even less the presence of technological intelligence. On the other hand, the detection of ET by radio, or by some other means, would, of necessity, guarantee the presence of both other habitable planets and the evolution elsewhere of another technological species.

First Planets

It has been a long wait for evidence. Astronomers have searched for decades for evidence of planets which orbit the nearest stars, but they had to wait until 1995 for the first confirmed discovery of a planet in orbit about another star.

The first of the six planets was discovered by Michel Mayor and Didier Queloz, of the Geneva Observatory, who found that the frequencies of light from the star 51 Pegasus were shifting in a periodic fashion. Such shifts in frequency, known as Doppler shifts, are commonly found in a range of different astronomical observations. For more than one-hundred years astronomers have used spectroscopes to study the spectral lines in the light from stars. Each element has its own specific set of lines which tell us what the stars are made of. The lines show as bright emission lines or as dark absorption lines, where the star's radiation is absorbed at certain wavelengths by elements in its outer layers (see Fig. 4.3).

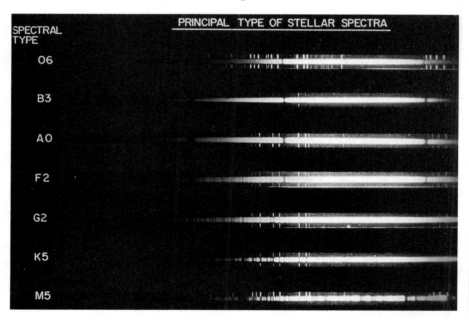

Fig. 4.3: The spectra of stars show, by their spectral lines, which ones are most like the Sun and therefore the best candidates for SETI observation. Döppler shifts in spectral lines indicate the directions and velocity of the star relative to us.

But these lines can also measure a star's velocity. The lines are shifted to the red when the star recedes (the well-known 'red-shift' of the Doppler effect) or to the violet part of the spectrum when it moves towards us. Astronomers have applied this phenomenon to study close pairs of stars (binary stars) which orbit each other. So close together are the stars of some binary systems that two stars shine as one. In some cases only shifts in the spectral lines have shown the presence of two stars, and have provided data on the mass and orbit of companion stars too faint to be observed. Astronomers have, therefore, used this method to detect planets. It's a convenient technique because the shifting spectral lines can be recorded almost as well from beneath the atmosphere as from above it. It's the only planet-seeking technique that doesn't work much better from space. The other advantage is that the close proximity of a planet to its star does not affect its detection. The proximity of planets to their stars poses formidable observational problems for astronomers. Planets are such small, dull objects, and stars so big and bright.

A Strange World

For more than a year, Mayor and Queloz monitored the Doppler shifts which showed that the star 51 Pegasus was in circular motion, completing one full circle every 4.23 days. (One should add here that our Sun would be observed to move in such a fashion, though not so drastically, if observed by astronomers in another planetary system see Fig. 4.4) The gravitational effect of a nearby body, a massive planet, was probably responsible. But of what kind? The application of mathematics provided the answer. The unseen companion was orbiting very close to 51 Pegasus – only one twentieth the distance of the Earth from the Sun – and it was just over half the mass of Jupiter. (Jupiter is more than three hundred times more massive than the Earth.)

This first detection of a planet in another planetary system was announced to the world at the beginning of 1996 at an astronomical conference in Texas. Over the years, there have been many false claims in the planet hunting business, and journalists have always been ready to cover these claims, telling the public that scientists have discovered a new Solar System. Michel Mayor and Didier Queloz had, therefore, checked and rechecked everything that could have misled them before making their formal announcement at an astronomical conference. Then the bubble burst. Mayor said he

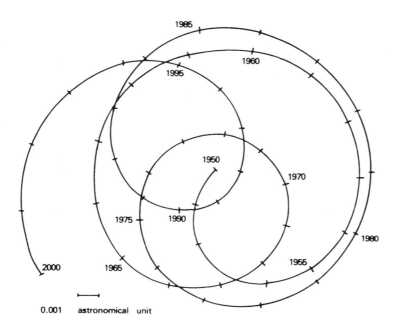

Fig. 4.4: The orbit of the Sun around the centre of mass of the Solar System from 1950 to the year 2000. The large loops, each averaging 12 years, are caused mainly by our most massive planets, Jupiter and Saturn. Alien astronomers would observe such a pattern with the Sun visible as a star with magnitude +1.1. Even Jupiter, our largest planet, would not be visible because the Sun is 250 million times brighter, but its effect on the Sun would be detectable.

received hundreds of phone calls, e-mails and faxes from around the world. One boy in America wanted to know if Mayor had yet visited the planet. As usual, journalists from around the world were mainly interested in knowing if there could be life on the planet.

Such an announcement could not be accepted without confirmation. Professor Geoffrey Marcy and Paul Butler, old hands in the planet-searching business, commenced work immediately with the Lick Observatory's Shane telescope, in California, and checked the Doppler shifts. "We found clear and incontrovertible evidence for a Jupiter-sized planet orbiting 51 Pegasus," said Marcy. The planet, according to Macey, is about as inhospitable as one could imagine. "The temperature of the planet's surface would be about 1,000 degrees Centigrade, due to the blazing light from its nearby sun. Neither liquid water nor organic molecules can exist at such temperatures."

No life, then, but how did the planet get so close to its star, and could it survive there? That was a puzzle. Peter Bodenheimer of the Lick Observatory did the necessary calculations to find out. Yes, the planet could remain intact for billions of years. It could even have been a little closer to its star and still have survived. The present theory is that the planet formed further out with a disc of dust and gas, something like Saturn and its rings. The gravitational pull of 51 Pegasus on the planet's disc then caused the planet to slow, and spiral inwards to its present orbit.

Having confirmed the existence of the first planet of another star, Geoffrey Marcy and Paul Butler began to analyse their own recorded data. For the past seven years, Marcy and Butler had been monitoring 60 neighbouring stars, and had just begun to observe another 60. From their data, which had been in the computer waiting to be analysed, they discovered two more planets. Each is several times the mass of Jupiter and orbits the sun-like stars 70 Virginis and 47 Ursa Majoris at about 35 light-years from Earth.

Marcy and Butler had made the mistake of assuming that the massive planets, the currently detectable planets of other systems, would be at great distances from their suns, as they are in the Solar System. Therefore, the orbital periods would be long, and any gravitational effects on a star would only be detectable from observations recorded over many years. Consequently, they hadn't rushed to analyse their data. No one guessed that the first confirmed planet of another star would be both massive and incredibly near its sun. But in science we should always expect the unexpected.

The planets discovered by Marcy and Butler would be slightly more hospitable than the first planet discovered, but nothing on Earth beyond bacteria could live there. The planet belonging to 47 Ursa Majoris is more than two-and-a-half times the mass of Jupiter, takes 1,100 days to orbit its star and has surface temperatures similar to those on Mars. If it were in the Solar System, its orbit would be between those of Mars and Jupiter. The planet of 70 Virginis is a whopper: 6½ times the mass of Jupiter and half the distance from its star as we are from the Sun. Its surface temperature is about 80 degrees Centigrade, so it could possess liquid water. We can't, therefore, absolutely deny the possibility of life – there are bacteria on Earth which thrive in hotter conditions.

The astronomers point out that such a massive planet could be a gas giant, like Jupiter, with no rocky surface. Nevertheless, we know that massive planets in the Solar System, because of their powerful gravitational fields, hold on to families of moons – mini Solar Systems, so to speak. And there's no reason to think that this arrangement is unique. In fact, the nature of gravity should make it universal. There could, conceivably, be planetary systems where the counterparts of Earth were, in fact, moons orbiting planets several times the mass of Jupiter. But such massive planets would have to be closer to their star (and an energy source) than Jupiter is to the Sun.

None of the six discovered planets is going to provide a home for the future, but the fact that they are orbiting neighbouring sun-like stars is very significant when we consider that the Galaxy (our Milky Way) is 100,000 million light-years across and contains more than a hundred billion stars. For every star we can see with the unaided eye there are 50 million which we cannot see. If a proportion of nearby stars have planets, then planets should exist throughout the Galaxy.

What if?

If the counterparts of our astronomers are out there, they could have been looking into space for a few billion years. The age of the oldest known sun-like stars gives them that amount of time to have evolved before us. In that case, did they find this blue planet of ours sometime after the atmosphere began to radiate its ozone and oxygen spectral lines? From what we know of geology and the history of life, that would have been from at least 350 million years ago. And if extraterrestrial astronomers had detected the Earth, what would have been their next steps in exploring such a discovery? If our astronomers in the future detected a blue planet in this way, the next step would surely be to send a probe, given that we had the resources available. Therefore, could evidence of those "next steps", taken by ET sometime during the past 350 million years, still be in existence? The possibility we currently have of detecting Earth-like planets around nearby stars raises this intriguing question, which we will examine later in some detail.

Infrared Planets

Potential planets are going to be small, dim objects and relatively close to large, bright objects – the stars they orbit. Even a dim star could be thousands of times brighter than its planets. Thus the great differences in luminosity make the separation of a planet from its star a major observational problem. Planet seekers have to be ready to cope with a probable separation equal only to one ten thousandth the diameter of the Moon as observed from Earth. Such optical astronomy is work for the future, when advanced astronomical technology can be established in space, or on the far side of the Moon. For the present, the astronomers use ingenuity and the equipment they have to detect planets comparable in mass to Jupiter.

Astronomers point out that visible light is not the best part of the electromagnetic spectrum for detecting the planets of other stars. A planet re-radiates in the infrared much of the energy it receives from its star. It can, therefore, be 1,000 times brighter in infrared than in visible light. In 1983, the Infrared Astronomical Satellite (IRAS) detected excessive infrared radiation from several dozen stars, in particular Vega, Formulhaut and Beta Pictoris (see cover photograph). The infrared was so intense that scientists believed it must come from orbiting discs of dust and debris. Such a disc provides a large radiating area. If the material in a disc formed planet-sized bodies, then the surface area radiating infrared would be greatly reduced, and the amount of radiation would not have been detectable by IRAS.

By chance, two American astronomers, Rich Terrile and Brad Smith, were carrying out an observational programme at the Las Campañas Observatory in Chile when they read a report of the IRAS discoveries. They happened to be in exactly the right place to photograph the star Beta Pictoris, which is fifty light-years away. Using a coronograph (an instrument designed to observe faint rings or nebulae around bright objects), Terrile and Smith obtained the most spectacular supporting evidence (available at the time) for the existence of other planetary systems. Beta Pictoris, they discovered, has a great disc of matter in orbit, twenty times the diameter of the Solar System. (see cover photograph) The evidence supported current theories that planets form within a stellar disc of gas and debris. However, no planet with advanced life will ever orbit Beta Pictoris, which is a young star, more massive and seven times more luminous than the Sun. Its mass means that its stable period will be very short compared with that of the Sun, and its radiation would be too intense for life as we know it.

Another method of searching for extra-solar planets has been developed by Don McCarthy and colleagues at the University of Arizona. They call it 'Near-Infrared Speckle Interferometry'. Put briefly, McCarthy takes several thousand frames of a star suspected of having a large planet, photographing at 100 frames a second. This brief exposure time 'freezes' the many speckles of light which normally make up the star's image. The 'speckles' are produced by turbulence in our atmosphere, but each 'frozen' speckle contains an image undistorted by atmospheric movement. All the information from the several thousand frames is then processed to provide one relatively clear picture.

Some of the most ambitious planet seekers work at the University of Arizona, where Roger Angel and others are planning a future infrared space telescope with a 16-metre diameter mirror – a very costly venture. It could remain on the drawing-board for years, but eventually something like it will be built and used to search for the spectral lines coming from the atmospheres of planets in other systems. Especially interesting would be the prominent spectral line of ozone in the infrared, signalling, as it would, the existence of Earth-like planets.

The point is that this line could only come from a rich oxygen atmosphere similar to our own. Plant life and photosynthesizing bacteria took about three billion years to put enough oxygen into the biosphere to form the ozone layer, which is only maintained by the continuous metabolic activity of photosynthesis. Remove the photosynthesizing bacteria and plants from Earth and the cycle would cease. Our oxygen and the ozone layer would disappear.

One could almost become fanciful here and suggest that nature has provided the prominent spectral line of ozone at 96,000 angstroms so that intelligent life can find other life in the universe. One can't help but think of the many "coincidences" in the values of the universal constants being precisely as they are. Change some of these (such as the charge on the electron being opposite and equal to the charge on the proton) and the universe as we know it could never have been. We would certainly not be here. The processes of the physical universe which have made our emergence possible have depended on the universal constants being exactly as they are. It's very strange, and currently inexplicable. It may, therefore, be taking speculation too far, but could the existence of the prominent ozone line be one more convenient "coincidence" in the great universal process? Probably not, but the presence of the prominent ozone line is so conveniently available, although we cannot yet use it to detect Earth-like planets. Nevertheless, it's there for the detection of other life, and, maybe, other intelligent beings.

Our ultimate concern may be the detection of other earths, but the spectral lines from the molecules which dominate other planetary atmospheres can also be detected, given the appropriate level of astronomical technology. Venus and Mars are characterized by the presence of carbon dioxide, and the four gas giants by the overwhelming presence of hydrogen compounds. So it should be possible, eventually, for astronomers to compare other planetary systems with our own by the study of the spectral lines observed.

In recent years I have spoken with numerous astronomers about their work to detect, in various ways, the presence of other planetary systems. They are all enthusiastic about the future of their line in astronomy, but the fact that the Earth could have been detected as a life-bearing planet from the spectral lines of its atmosphere for about the past 350 million years is not something they have ever raised. They will show enthusiasm about the prospect of astronomy being able to detect Earth-like planets by this method, given a couple of decades and the necessary financial support, but the possibility of having been beaten at this game by a hundred million years or more by astronomers of another life-form seems never to have crossed their minds. At least, the implications of such discoveries have not been speculated upon.

However, our galaxy is a hundred million light-years across, and we need to discover the location of the nearest other earth. Astronomers don't yet have the equipment to search for other earths, but it can be developed, and the planets just discovered, which indicate that the formation of planets is a universal process, should provide enough incentive to press ahead with the necessary technological developments.

Life and Atmospheres

The evolution of the Earth's atmosphere and the evolution of life have been inseparable, the one continually affecting the development of the other. Life, the atmosphere, the Earth's land surface and oceans are all one system. We are beginning to appreciate that for such a system to develop continuously for four billion years, as it has here, a planet would have to orbit a star of about the same mass as the Sun. And planets with advanced life-forms may have masses similar to that of the Earth, whilst their orbits may fall within a rather narrow zone. Outside that narrow zone, they may not remain continuously habitable, although many may have life which evolves for millions of years. It could be that Mars can illustrate this point for us, if we should find there, in ancient sedimentary rocks, fossilised microbes that would confirm the claim that evidence of life exists in meteorite ALH84001, which almost certainly came from Mars, but more on that later. (The possibility of live microbes existing kilometres beneath the Martian surface is another subject which we need to consider in the next chapter.) The point for us here is that Mars orbits just outside the theoretical habitable zone for the Solar System.

Until the early 1970s, it was widely accepted that an atmosphere for the origin and evolution of life progressed from one rich in basic hydrogen compounds to its chemical opposite, an atmosphere with abundant oxygen. Laboratory experiments had repeatedly shown that a hydrogen-dominated atmosphere promotes the formation of the basic molecules of life. Many of these molecules form automatically when energy is injected. Any energy will do: electricity, heat or radiation. Similar experiments using an oxygen atmosphere, which is essential for the evolution of advanced organisms, produce none of the molecular units of life. Life, it seems, cannot form in an oxidising atmosphere, one with free oxygen, although it needs that kind of atmosphere later. At least it has on Earth.(see Figs. 4.5 and 4.6)

Astronomers concluded many years ago that hydrogen and helium, the lightest and by far the most abundant of the elements, were driven from the Earth by solar radiation, probably as the Earth formed. Consequently, the accepted theory is that the Earth's first atmosphere came from its hot interior, from intense volcanic activity. Most astronomers and geologists think that the first atmosphere was composed of carbon dioxide, nitrogen and water vapour. This ties in with what we know about the atmospheres of Venus and Mars. The Earth never had a hydrogen-dominated atmosphere, which it was once assumed to have had, even though the primordial solar disc would have been composed mainly of hydrogen.

Only the evolution of photosynthesizing organisms (and photosynthesis is a formidably complex chemical process to evolve) provided the oxygen atmosphere that eventually made the evolution of advanced animal life possible. On Earth it was photosynthesizing bacteria (sometimes misleadingly called blue-green algae) which first began to put oxygen into the atmosphere, and did so for a couple of billion years before higher forms of plant life began to evolve and added to the process (see Figs. 4.7 and 4.8) The Earth's atmosphere has, therefore, been completely changed, although there must always have existed enough atmosphere to prevent the escape of volatile molecules like water.

THE SEARCH FOR EXTRATERRESTRIAL INTELLIGENCE

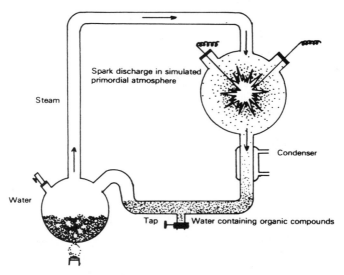

Spark discharge in simulated primordial atmosphere

Steam

Water

Condenser

Tap

Water containing organic compounds

Fig. 4.5: Dr Stanley Miller's classic 1953 experiment on the origin of life was based on the assumption that the Earth's primordial atmosphere was composed of hydrogen and its compounds, such as methane and ammonia – the kind of atmosphere possessed by Jupiter. When such an atmosphere is simulated in a laboratory in a closed system such as this, many of the building blocks form automatically. This sort of experiment has been repeated many times using various forms of energy such as UV, radioactivity and heat. All produced similar results.

Ozone and Land Life

Research suggests that an ozone layer could not have formed until an oxygen atmosphere comparable to what exists today was being maintained by photosynthesis. (Ozone is a molecule of three oxygen atoms.) The evidence from geology and palaeontology suggests that this would have been soon after 400 million years ago, just before a certain group of fishes began to evolve into amphibians, which began the colonization of dry land. Dry land would not previously have been tolerable habitat for them. There is fossil evidence of insects and mites dated at more than 400 million old, but such small creatures would have found plenty of shielding under stones and rocks. From the fossil record, however, it appears that there were no candidate organisms, living under the protection of water, that were ready to go out and colonize dry land before the ozone layer had formed. It therefore looks like a coincidence that the ozone layer formed shortly

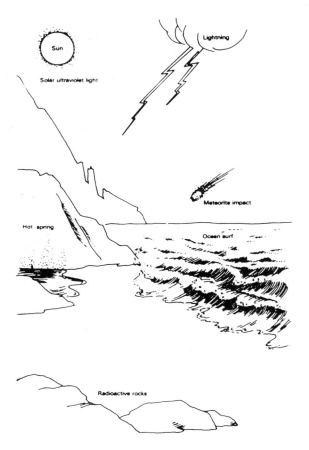

Fig 4.6: Possible sources of energy for the origin of life on the primordial Earth.

before the evolution of land animals. The timing of its formation may not have held evolution back in any way.

The fossil record tells us that life, from its unknown origin some 4 billion years ago, continued only at a bacterial level for about 2 billion years. We can see the bacteria in the rocks of this period, during which new structures and complex chemistries, used later by more advanced life, must have evolved. The first advanced cells (eucaryotic cells which are far more complex than bacteria), the kind of cells from which all many-celled organisms from mushrooms to ourselves are formed, can first be seen in rocks about 1½ billion years old. It now looks as if these advanced single-celled organisms evolved

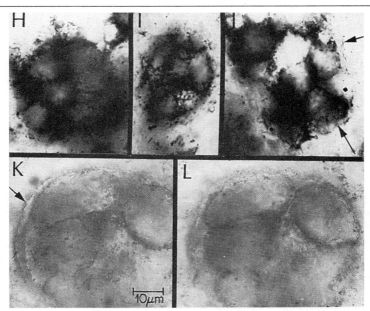

Fig 4.7: Fossilised bacteria from North-Western Australia, dated at between 3.3 and 3.5 billion years old are probably the oldest known sheath-enclosed colonies of cells. They appear to have been photosynthesisising bacteria, like today's cyanobactreia (below)

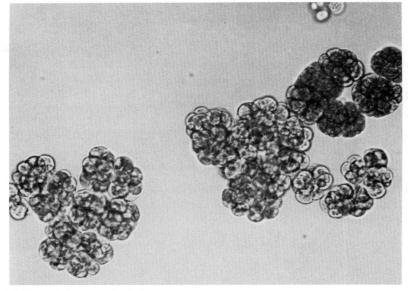

Fig. 4.8: Present-day cyanobacteria

from a coming together (symbiosis) of different kinds of ancient bacteria.

From our time (that is $3\frac{1}{2}$ billion years on from the earliest known fossils of bacteria) we can see a well-defined path in the history of life on Earth, though not a predetermined path. We know that because of the way evolution works that path can never be the same on any other habitable world, but could the path followed by life elsewhere often be approximately similar? We shall never know until some extraterrestrials tell us their evolutionary histories, if they ever do. We do know, however, that life which can photosynthesize must come before an oxygen atmosphere, and an oxygen atmosphere must come before an ozone layer, which must come before the colonization of dry land by large animals and the evolution of technologically intelligent animals. The latter, of course, are not guaranteed. By the way, we should not expect the complex chemical machinery of photosynthesis on Earth to be precisely duplicated on other worlds. The scientists in this field will tell you that, chemically speaking, there is plenty of scope for life to evolve different versions (see Fig. 4.9).

Fossils tell a Strange Story

In 1986, at the University of California, Professor J. William Schopf announced the discovery of fossils of oxygen-producing bacteria, photosynthesizing bacteria, in rocks found near Port Hedland in Western Australia (see Fig. 4.7). There is also abundant evidence of bacteria in ancient rocks of various ages elsewhere, but the earliest indirect evidence of life, in the form of organic molecules that only living processes could have produced, actually exists in rocks some 3.8 billion years old.

Without the pioneering research of a very few scientists, including William Schopf, we could not have known that life on Earth consisted only of micro-organisms for the first three billion years after its origin. That is, for about three-quarters of life's history. Few 'advanced' life-forms appear in the fossil record until the beginning of the Cambrian Period, 570 million years ago, although older fossils have been discovered at some rare sites dating back to about 650 million years ago, in what is called the Late Precambrian. No fossils of plants of this age have so far been found anywhere, but they must have flourished in the shallow seas and lakes of the time. Many of the animal fossils look like small jellyfish (see Fig. 4.10), and may be the

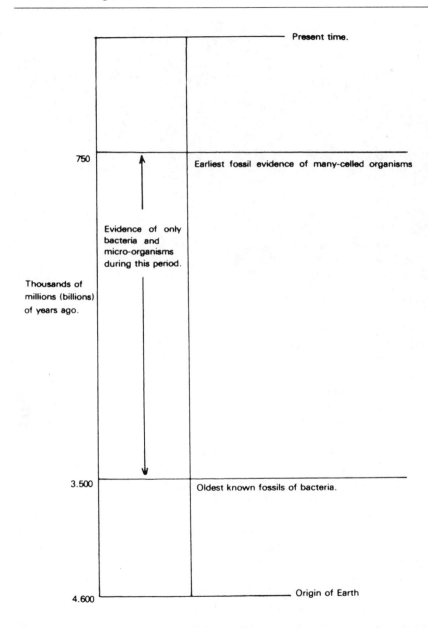

Fig. 4.9: Why did it take so long for life to progress from single-celled microbes to the first many-celled organisms? The gap of almost three billion years when apparently nothing but single-celled organisms existed on Earth has presented quite a puzzle.

Fig. 4.10: An example of one of the oldest-known fossils of a many-celled organism, discovered by Dr John Cope and his students at a site near Carmarthen, South Wales.

ancestors of present-day jellyfish. There are also tiny fossils of animals with jointed limbs (arthropods), the ancestors of the crustaceans and insects, and fossilised tracks made by worms or sluglike creatures in the ancient mud. We can, therefore, see that by 650 million years ago animals had already evolved complex bodies composed of many different types of cells. And complex bodies have to be controlled. When we look at the fossils of these ancient creatures we cannot, of course, see any nerve cells, but they must have possessed nervous systems like those found in their present-day counterparts.

It was during Cambrian times (570 to 500 million years ago) that a wonderful variety of aquatic life-forms evolved. All the basic types of advanced animal life can be found in the Cambrian fossils, and some which no longer exist. Anyone can see them in our museums of natural history. There is, nevertheless, an unresolved question hanging over the fossils of the oldest known ancestors of one group of animals – our group, the vertebrates. Richard Jefferies in his research on the calcichordates at the British Museum (Natural History) in London, spent some 25 years trying to trace the ancestry of the vertebrates in the fossil record, and has been the major researcher in this field in Britain. As he once told me, however, you can count the number of leading scientists involved in the origin of the vertebrates on the fingers of one hand. It's not a commercial activity; only a fundamental one for our knowledge and understanding of biology, if we want to know where we all came from (see Fig. 4.11).

Fig 4.11: A primitive *calchichordate*, one of a large group of strange creatures which lived in the mud of shallow seas 600-400 million years ago. Some members of this group may have given rise to the ancestors of all background animals.

The Great Gap

A gap of three billion years between the first single-celled organisms, the first bacteria, and the abundant variety of life in Cambrian times needs an explanation. The best one we have is that it took that amount of time for there to be enough oxygen in the atmosphere, oceans and lakes for advanced life-forms to evolve. But a great deal of complex chemistry must have evolved in ancient bacteria, much of which is still used by life today. The structural complexity of advanced cells, which first appeared in single-celled organisms $1\frac{1}{2}$ billion years ago, is remarkable, a fact that could not have been fully appreciated before the electron microscope.

We are only just beginning to appreciate the significance of this pattern of evolution, which suggests the possibility that there may have been a parallel development of microbial life on Mars in its early days, until an irreversible ice age overcame that planet a few billion years ago. Life might have flourished there while water in liquid form, rather than ice, remained on the planet. There would have been no need of oxygen in the Martian atmosphere. There was no free oxygen in the primordial atmosphere of the Earth. Indeed, when the first photosynthesising bacteria began to put oxygen into the atmosphere, as a waste product of their photosynthesizing metabolism, it was a gas toxic to other micro-organisms.

Stable Stars for ET

The message from the history of life on Earth is that creatures capable of building spaceships could only evolve where their star (sun) remains stable for several billions of years. This is the period when a star 'burns' hydrogen to form helium, thus producing energy by the nuclear fusion reaction of the H-bomb. This is the main part of a star's life cycle. Astronomers know that the more massive a star is, the quicker it consumes its hydrogen in this way and leaves its stable period. They have calculated that a star consumes its hydrogen fuel at a rate roughly equal to the cube of the star's mass (m^3) in stars that are more than three times the mass of the Sun. Thus a star that is ten times more massive than the Sun 'burns' its hydrogen to helium and passes through its stable period a thousand times faster than a star like the Sun. It will remain stable for only ten million years compared with the ten billion years calculated for the Sun, although astronomers tell us that the Sun will make the Earth too hot for life in less than another billion years. No chance, therefore, for technological intelligence to evolve on planets belonging to stars much more massive than the Sun, when even small differences in the mass of stars so greatly affect the time during which they could support habitable planets. Even a star just 25 per cent more massive than the Sun would end its stable period at about the same age as the Sun is today.

The stable periods of stars range from a few million years for O-type stars, the most massive and brightest stars, to many billions of years for M-type stars, the least massive and least luminous. The Sun, a G2 star, has already passed through half its stable period, but the stable period of an M-type star will be more than the present age of the Galaxy. However, M-type stars may be incapable of possessing Earth-type planets for a reason other than stability. The orbital zone for habitable planets to evolve (the so-called habitable zone) may be either too narrow or non-existent.

The historical development of astronomical nomenclature means that stars are now classified by the letters O, B, A, F, G, K, M. O-type stars are the most massive; M-type stars the least massive. After M there used to be R,N and S-type stars, classifications now discarded. The old mnemonic for star classification used to be, 'O, Be A Fine Girl Kiss Me Right Now, Sweetie,' but this no longer requires the last three words.

Although we call the Sun an average star, more than 85 per cent of stars are less massive and less luminous, which means they will remain stable longer, but only a small proportion of these stars may have habitable planets. Also, more than 75 per cent of all stars are part of double or multiple star systems. There may be planets in such systems, but their orbits could make them unsuitable for life. It depends on how close the stars are to each other in double or multiple systems. Planets with stable biospheres may be possible in double systems where the two stars are very close to each other, so that a family of planets could orbit the two stars as if they were one.

If we look at Jupiter and the Sun, we can see how habitable planets might be possible in a double system where the two stars are well separated. Jupiter is 320 times the mass of the Earth and 2.5 times the mass of all the other bodies of the Solar System combined, excluding the Sun. Jupiter also has what amounts to a planetary system of its own in its family of moons.

If Jupiter had been about fifty times more massive, the hydrogen at its core would have become hot enough to start nuclear fusion. Jupiter would then have been a red dwarf star, like the many red dwarfs in the neighbourhood of the Sun. Had such a small, dim star existed instead of Jupiter, it would probably not have adversely affected the evolution of life on Earth, but the presence of massive stars in double and multiple systems could prevent the evolution of habitable planets. Stars several times more massive than the Sun would also end their stable periods in nuclear outbursts of inconceivable magnitude, which would surely destroy life on any planets.

With stars of the Sun's mass (and less), the prospects for habitable planets in double and multiple systems seem better. Robert Harrington of the US Naval Observatory, Washington DC, calculated in a computer study that the orbits of planets in double star systems could be very stable. Harrington then tested his results on the Solar System. He replaced the Sun by two stars, each half the mass of the Sun and separated by 0.4 astronomical units. (An astronomical unit is the average Earth-Sun distance.) Mercury, the nearest planet to the change, was very upset and soon left the Solar System, whilst Venus changed its orbit slightly. All the other planets continued as they are.

Harrington also replaced Jupiter with a star of the same mass as the Sun in order to discover the effect on the inner planets. Again, it was only the closest planet to the change, Mars, which suffered. Mars behaved very badly. Its orbit became unstable and it looked as if it would eventually leave the system, but the other inner planets remained in their present orbits.

However, the presence of another sun (of equal mass and luminosity to the Sun) at the distance of Jupiter would surely have affected the evolution of life, even if its gravitational influence on the Earth's orbit was insignificant. Life's adaptations to light would have been different, and the extra heat, even though from the distance of Jupiter, may have made conditions too warm for advanced life on dry land.

Narrow Escapes for Earth

The evolution of atmospheres and habitable planets seems more complicated than was previously supposed. Michael Hart, when at NASA's Goddard Space Flight Center, showed, in theory, just how precariously balanced may be the physical conditions on which the Earth's development rests. According to his studies, the Earth almost did not become a habitable world at all, narrowly escaping catastrophe on two occasions. Hart's study does not claim to show what did happen, but it does show what could have happened, and draws our attention to the demanding set of circumstances which appear to be needed for the evolution of an Earth-like planet with a biosphere which remains stable for life during about 4 billion years. Hart ran his computer program, working through dozens of different Earth histories, starting each with a different set of conditions to find which set best fitted what we know of Earth history and present conditions. The Earth's age in the study was 4.6 billion years, the age which geologists and astronomers accept as established by radioactive dating techniques, using Earth and Moon rocks and meteorites for their research.

Hart's study showed that water clouds completely covered our planet within the first 150 million years of its history. These clouds existed in an atmosphere 1.5 times denser than today's, and by 3.5 billion years ago had helped to bring the Earth's temperature to a critical point. As on Venus, where a very dense atmosphere keeps the planet's surface several times hotter than boiling water, the primordial atmosphere of Earth stopped heat from the Sun being radiated back into space. At this stage in the computer study, the Earth almost turned into a second Venus. Hart wrote, "Had the Earth been slightly closer to the Sun a runaway greenhouse effect would have occurred fairly early in the Earth's history."

The Earth was saved by the first photosynthesizing bacteria (blue-green algae or, more precisely, cyanobacteria). These micro-organisms, which must have evolved from earlier bacteria, possessed the first chemical machinery for synthesizing the molecules they needed for growth, using sunlight as their energy source. Like the plant life which later evolved, simple inorganic chemicals and sunlight were all they needed.

As photosynthesizing bacteria used up carbon dioxide in the atmosphere, making organic molecules for their growth and reproduction, the effectiveness of the atmospheric heat trap decreased – and the Earth's temperature. By 2.75 billion years ago, the clouds had broken up and the atmosphere was half its present density. By about two billion years ago, photosynthesizing organisms had released enough oxygen into the atmosphere to begin to oxidise rocks for the first time. The familiar red deposits of iron oxide are one example. With less atmosphere to retain the Sun's heat, the Earth then began to cool. Within five million years, ice sheets covered 10 percent of an Earth heading towards an irreversible ice age.

"Had the Earth's orbit been slightly larger," wrote Hart, "then runaway glaciation would have occurred about two billion years ago." The study indicated that an increase in the Earth-Sun distance of just 1 per cent would have been sufficient, and that the Earth came within one degree Centigrade of becoming permanently frozen. Hart's results, therefore, predict that Mars, which is further from the Sun, should have long ago experienced this runaway glaciation. Indeed, the investigations of Mars have shown the existence of a permanent ice age there, and any large quantity of water, if such exists, is now locked in ice beneath the planet's surface.

Not until 420 million years ago, according to the study, was there enough oxygen and ozone (composed of three oxygen atoms) in the Earth's atmosphere to form the ozone layer which subsequently shielded dry land from the Sun's intense ultraviolet radiation, and allowed life to leave the protection of water for the first time. It should be noted that the first life-forms to colonize dry land were probably not ready to do so before 420 million years ago. They were not waiting under water for the ozone layer to form. As we know, land plants must have established themselves first, before invertebrate animals. Later a group of lung fishes came onto the muddy borders of lakes and rivers, which periodically dried up, and these evolved into the first amphibians some 350 million years ago.

So, are the majority of potential earths, orbiting stars like the Sun, caught by one of the two runaway processes, becoming permanently frozen worlds like Mars or planetary furnaces like Venus? It's a question Hart's work provokes. The idea that, for the origin and evolution of life, a planet had only to occupy a suitable orbit around its star, the so-called habitable zone, where the temperature range enabled water to be liquid, now looks too simple.

No High Gravity Technologist

Theory indicates that planets for advanced life must also have a mass within a limited range. The science fiction idea of highly intelligent creatures as flat as pancakes, living on a massive planet with several times the gravity of Earth, looks biologically and astronomically impossible. Active creatures that might eventually evolve into technologists would need an atmosphere with plenty of oxygen to give them energy, and planets much more massive than the Earth could not evolve such an atmosphere. Theoretical studies indicate that a planet, which orbits in a habitable zone, must also have a radius and mass within a certain range to avoid either the greenhouse effect or permanent glaciation. To support life for several billion years (like the Earth), and evolve an oxygen-rich atmosphere, a planet cannot have a gravity much less than 80 per cent of 1g or much greater than 120 per cent of 1g.

We might even ask the question, "Can rocky planets, far more massive than the Earth, form around stars like the Sun?" Of course, we cannot know how often enough heavy elements are present around young stars to form really gigantic rocky planets, but we can note that within the Solar System the Earth is the largest rocky planet, and that the gas giants are much more massive because they formed at a greater distance from the heat of the Sun and, therefore, could retain so much hydrogen and helium. The Earth, being relatively close to the Sun, easily lost these light elements. Four of the planets discovered in 1995-96 are massive and closer to their stars than the Earth is to the Sun. But, for the present, we don't know if they are gas giants or rocky planets, or if they formed in their present orbits.

Stars for Earth-Like Planets

For many years it was thought that F, G, K and M stars could all possess habitable planets. Each class of star, by the way, is subdivided into ten, so that there are, for example, G-type stars from G0 to G9. The lower the number, the more massive and luminous the star. The habitable zone for planets, so it was supposed, would be broader and more distant for F-type stars, and nearer and narrower around the less luminous M-type stars. However, according to Hart's second computer study, the continuously habitable zone becomes narrower as stars become less massive, and such a zone no longer exists with stars having a mass less than 83 per cent that of the Sun. This suggests that the majority of stars, and the majority are less massive than the Sun, may have no continuously habitable planets, though, of course, they may have planets.

Hart's study also showed that stars just 10 per cent more massive than the Sun will emit too much ultraviolet radiation after four billion years for life to be able to establish itself on land. According to this, had the Sun been 10 per cent more massive there would have been no land life on Earth. Potentially habitable planets with suns 20 per cent more massive than the Sun will also become too hot for life. Almost all planets, so the study showed, may therefore become either too hot or too cold before intelligent life has time to evolve.

Only a small percentage of planets, therefore, which have suns with masses within about 10 per cent of the Sun's mass, have a chance of becoming Earth-like. Even then it is only a chance, for they must also have appropriate mass and also be within a rather narrow orbital zone. Otherwise, they cannot evolve an oxygen atmosphere and provide a continuously habitable home for advanced life. It could be, therefore, that planets for intelligent life, whose hypothetical abundance has often been entertained by scientists in the SETI community, may not be abundant after all. This conclusion is pessimistic compared with other estimates on the numbers of habitable planets, but it's probably better to be pessimistic rather than optimistic.

In any case, if advances in space technology lead to the colonization of lifeless planets and moons, the abundance or otherwise of worlds like the Earth may be irrelevant, as far as the possible number of civilizations in the Galaxy is concerned. One civilization on an Earth-like planet could have established itself on many other worlds, given an adequate transport system for interstellar voyages.

Exotic Habitats for Life

So far our concern has been with rocky planets, worlds with solid surfaces for life to evolve, but there are the gas giants as well. A gas giant is a very different type of planet, mostly atmosphere and no planetary surface. The four gas giants of the Solar System (Jupiter, Saturn, Uranus and Neptune) are massive and their high gravitational fields have retained much of their primordial atmospheres, which at certain depths must be as dense as water. We can, therefore, ask ourselves if these worlds could provide a niche for life, though not for technological life. Could the two distinct types of planet, one wonders, provide two distinct types of environment for life throughout the universe? According to astronomical theory, other planetary systems should include both gas giants and rocky planets.

Before speculating about the gas giants themselves, we should consider the exotic moons Europa and Titan, both of which are about the size of our moon. Europa is Jupiter's second major moon, a world completely covered by a crust of smooth white and brownish ice, which may be tens of kilometres thick. Unlike most moons in the Solar System, Europa is devoid of craters, showing that its surface is being constantly renewed, presumably by liquid bursting through the enormous cracks on its surface. Some cracks stretch across Europa for hundreds of miles. The images from the Galileo spacecraft show cracks which are darkish with a white line running down their centre. The geologists suggest that "dirty geysers" erupt, throwing up a mixture of ice and darker substances along the line of a crack. This is then followed by a slow and continuous flow of clean water or ice which "paints" the white line between the two darker lines.

So is there a continuous ocean of liquid water and/or warm ice beneath Europa's icy crust? (Warm ice would be ice not far below freezing point.) Liquid water could be present because of the immensely powerful mechanism – the gravitational field of Jupiter – which cracks the thick ice. Jupiter's gravitational field is ever present and must produce tides within Europa. The movement of these tides will produce heat. (The same gravitational field produces huge volcanic eruptions on Io, one of Jupiter's other moons.)

The spectacular nature of Europa was first observed by NASA's Voyager 2 spacecraft in 1979. The first photographs of this world shocked everyone. Now, in 1996, with the Galileo spacecraft, NASA has returned to gather more information than it could with the Voyager missions. Ronald Greeley, a geologist and one of the imaging

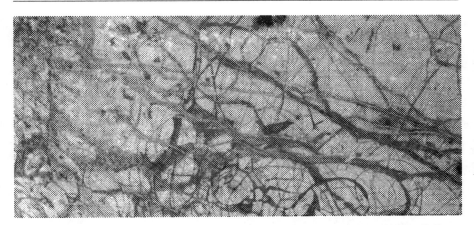

Fig 4.12: The broken ice on the surface of Europa, taken on June 27, 1996 by NASA's Galileo spacecraft. Europa has a shell of water up to 60 miles thick and the icy crust has broken into plates up to 18.5 miles across. The smallest visible feature is about 1 mile wide.

team, said, "This moon is a marvellous place. We're seeing evidence of a lot of geological activity. In some areas the ice is broken up into large pieces that have shifted away from one another, but they obviously fit together like a jigsaw puzzle. This shows the ice crust has been, or still is, lubricated from below by warm ice or maybe liquid water." (see Fig. 4.12)

The big question for NASA is whether a niche for life exists beneath the icy crust? Ronald Greeley, for one, is optimistic that we shall have an answer. "We want to go back to some areas of Europa that suggest the presence of soft ice or liquid water under the ice, and test some of the questions we're currently asking."

Galileo will be working in the Jupiter system for some time, but won't be sampling the waters of Europa for life on this mission, though it's a fascinating future prospect. We currently have no idea what could happen in a liquid environment beneath Europa's crust. There could exist a vast icy ocean there, although it would probably be one with no dissolved oxygen, unlike the oceans of Earth. But life on Earth did manage without free oxygen in the atmosphere and oceans for more than a billion years. As a potential home for life beyond Earth, Europa is almost as good as Mars.

Saturn's largest moon, Titan, due for future investigations, is a very different world from Europa and any other moon in the Solar System. Its orange atmosphere of methane-ice, nitrogen and organic molecules is 1.5 times the density of our atmosphere. Astronomers are working on the problems of Titan, but current theory is that the orange atmosphere may hide a sea of methane and ethane one kilometre deep. This exotic sea may cover Titan completely, perhaps with a top crust of water-ice crystals and organic materials. Titan is a very cold world – the sunlight falling there is only one hundredth of that which falls on Earth – but it is a fascinating subject for planetary scientists and organic chemists.

Although the gas giants have no surface, apart from their cloud tops, there may be layers in their atmospheres where pressures and temperatures produce ocean-like environments. The deeper a layer is in the atmosphere, the hotter it is, so that where a water layer coincides with the right pressure and temperature range there could exist 'atmospheric oceans' for organic chemistry. Such oceans would be thousands of times larger in volume than the seas of the primordial Earth. This is a highly speculative scenario, although there is indirect evidence from the fly-past of Voyager 2 that Uranus has a layer of hot water some 5,000 miles beneath its surface clouds. The main source of this water is thought to be comets, which have been described as 'huge dirty snowballs'. Both Uranus and Neptune are more vulnerable to collisions with comets than Earth because of their high gravitational attraction, and because they are nearer to the source of comets at the boundary of the Solar System. The present position is that more data is needed from planetary probes to check on these preliminary findings.

Jupiter and Saturn are hotter than Uranus, although they receive little heat from the Sun. Both radiate internal heat, which has been explained provisionally by very slow gravitational contraction. They therefore appear to offer the opportunity to see the results of more than four billion years of organic chemistry. Laboratory experiments on primordial atmospheres, of the kind possessed by Jupiter and Saturn, have produced some of the molecules of life with colours that match the brownish reds of Jupiter and Saturn.

The build-up of organic molecules to a point where life could form may have been prevented on, or rather in, Jupiter and Saturn because their internal heat creates powerful convection currents – Jupiter radiates about three times as much heat as it receives from the Sun, and Saturn twice as much. The signs of convection currents are obvious in NASA's photographs of Jupiter and Saturn, and any organic molecules building up in complexity would, therefore, be carried upwards to lower temperatures and pressures and then downwards to certain incineration. But do layers of water exist in the gas giants? A probe from the Galileo spacecraft, which descended 400 miles into Jupiter's atmosphere in 1996, found no evidence of water. The basic question, therefore, remains unanswered: do any layers of atmosphere in any of the gas giants possess the right substances for life where an appropriate range in temperature exists?

At present we can only speculate in the absence of adequate information that life in gas giants in planetary systems could be even more interesting than life on another terrestrial-type planet like Mars. Gas giants would not, however, be planets for technological ETs. This would be more unlikely than a technological species evolving in the sea, where at least there is a sea-bed with a wide range of habitats and materials for potential technology. The long history of life in our oceans seems to provide proof that a technological intelligence cannot evolve in a watery environment.

What, one wonders, would become of life forced to continue to evolve in a primordial hydrogen-dominated atmosphere? Would it remain in microbial form, as certain microbes have which continue to live in oxygen-free habitats on Earth – to live in the primordial way? Or is it simply that the limited range of habitats on Earth which are still devoid of oxygen restricts their present-day inhabitants to the microscopic? For all we know, evolution in a permanent primordial atmosphere, like that of a gas giant, might create a rich range of life, though it seems unlikely because the range of habitats would be very limited in a gas giant. From this speculation we can play with the idea that life, like planets, falls into two main categories: primary life in primary life-zones, and secondary life like ours, which lives in a planet's second atmosphere. Whatever the truth may be, the gas giants are fascinating places about which we know too little at the present time.

Gas Giant Ecosystems

In 1976, Carl Sagan and E.E. Salpeter, at Cornell University, published a long paper on the possible evolution of life on, or rather in, Jupiter. They suggested that ecological niches could exist in Jupiter for sinking, floating and hunting organisms – in short, a balanced ecosystem. An objection to their idea is that although such different organisms might maintain a balanced ecosystem, the floaters and hunters would have had to evolve in the same niche in which the sinkers live like the phytoplankton in our oceans. As far as we can imagine, no other niche exists in a gas giant. There the analogy with the ocean ends because our floaters (jellyfish and the like) and hunters (fish and many invertebrates) did not, and could not, have evolved in the surface waters of the oceans where our phytoplankton live. The same would presumably apply to the evolution of organisms in a gas giant.

Intriguing though the prospect of life in gas giants may be, our concern is really with planets where ETs capable of technology may evolve. From our knowledge of evolution in the oceans it seems that a similar environment in a gas giant could not produce technological intelligence, nor could an Earth-like planet which was completely and permanently covered by water. It does look as if dry land may be the only route to technological life and civilization. On dry land, we at least know that the necessary biological attributes can evolve.

Chapter Five

Life and ET

When Richard Dawkins, a leading authority on evolutionary biology, was commenting on the announcement, at the beginning of 1996, that three planets had been detected in orbit about three nearby stars, the media immediately wanted to know if there was life out there. After all, these were the first planets beyond the Solar System to be detected. The planets detected were about as massive as Jupiter and not candidates for life, but the line from those in astronomical SETI was that the discovery of any sort of planets around nearby stars indicated that Earth-like planets should be in orbit about some of the few billion other sun-like stars in the Galaxy. Dawkins maintained that this did not follow, that the Copernican revolution which began in the 15th century, may not extend to showing that our world civilization is only one among many others in the Galaxy, and vastly more in the universe as a whole. Yes, there are billions of galaxies like our Milky Way, and in our galaxy alone there are billions of stars like the Sun, but are there billions of planets like the Earth?

"Just suppose," said Dawkins, "that stars with planets really are fantastically rare. Suppose that, in a universe of a billion billion stars, there really is only one star that has a watery planet, bubbling with the right organic mix to generate DNA or some equivalent. That ultra-unique star, that star in a billion billion, simply has to be our Sun. Why? Because here we are talking about it… By itself, therefore, the fact that life exists here tells us nothing about how likely life is to exist elsewhere."

If no other planet exists in the Galaxy with the physical conditions suitable for the origin and continued support of life, then Dawkins is correct in what he says, but this runs directly against the most fascinating fundamental development in our thinking during the past few decades. We know that billions of stars like the Sun exist, and, with the recent detection of planets beyond the Solar System (the score has since risen to six in 1996), we know that other planetary systems of some sort exist within 35 light-years of Earth. Put this against the fact that our galaxy is 100 million lights years across, and we can see that those six planetary systems, plus our own, exist in just a minute sample of galactic space.

An Inevitable Phenomenon?

We know that life formed here some 4 billion years ago, apparently as soon as physical conditions made it possible. Had there been a long period of time, say a couple of billion years before life arose, our view of life would be very different. We also know that life has been remarkably robust in the face of a whole series of climatic and geological catastrophes. It is no feeble phenomenon.

It also seems that the inherent nature of physics and chemistry, which are universal, provide all the molecular building blocks automatically, given the right conditions. Numerous biologists have searched for the mechanism which formed the first self-reproducing molecular complexes and started life on its evolutionary future. They haven't found it yet, as far as anyone knows for certain, though there is no shortage of theories. But one can believe, and at this stage we have to rest a little on belief, that the mechanism must be as inevitable in its operation as the mechanisms which formed the galaxies and the stars and planets, and, through the nuclear reactions within stars, forged all the elements essential for the formation of life.

The mechanism which starts life on its evolutionary way, anywhere in the universe, should be inevitable. Otherwise the phenomenon of life does not fit into the "great scheme of things", as the galaxies, stars and planets seem to do. Everything on Earth seems to have been prepared for the origin of life, so why not elsewhere? If the physical and chemical mechanism which produced the first life on Earth turns out not to have been inevitable, that it has depended on something approaching a freak event, then the origin of life does not fit in with the pattern followed by the universe up to that point, and we would be wasting our time searching for evidence of ET.

The Universal Road to Complexity

The widespread circumstantial evidence is strongly against the hypothesis of life as an event unique to the Earth. From the origin of life came the formation of literally thousands of complex molecular units which fit together so precisely, and function so perfectly, that life looks like an advanced part of the unfolding of the universe from the formation of galaxies to the evolution of intelligent creatures, who may eventually become fully aware of the nature of the universe. One process just leads to another and it all looks inevitable, given a certain set of starting conditions when time and the universe began. So where is that mechanism which started life on Earth, and would it inevitably start life on any other planet with the right conditions?

Are there Martians down below?

The study of the most ancient rock formations of Mars is a top priority for those in SETI. The photographic evidence suggests that abundant water once flowed on that world. In its early days, the red planet may have been more Earth-like than red, and it may have continued to evolve in that way for a billion years or more before its permanent ice age set in. Thus, fossilized microscopic life could exist in its rocks because fossils of bacteria exist in our rocks which are 3.5 billion years old.

NASA's announcement, in August 1996, that their scientists had discovered fossils of bacteria-like organisms in one of the twelve SNC meteorites surprised everyone. The SNC meteorites, which have chemical characteristics that match those discovered by the two Viking Landers on Mars in 1976, have been accepted as Martian material only in the past few years. Amongst the SNC meteorites, however, meteorite ALH84001 is the only one to show signs of past life. It was found in 1984, although its Martian origin was not recognised until 1993 (see Fig. 5.1).

Research teams at the Johnson Space Center and Stanford University, aided by six other NASA and university partners, dated the material and possible fossils within the four pound meteorite at 3.6 billion years old. That's a hundred million years older than the oldest known evidence of fossilized bacteria in Earth rocks.

This was not the first time that scientists had claimed to have discovered evidence of life in a meteorite. My mind went back to a time in 1961 when I reported on the research of Dr. Bartholomew Naga of Fordham University, in New York. His group had analysed a piece of rock from the Orgueil meteorite and found distinct signs of life. Numerous scientists had studied the Orgueil meteorite which

Fig. 5.1: Meteorite ALH84001 (Johnson Space Center)

had broken into fragments in the atmosphere and landed in France in 1864. It had been especially interesting, even in the last century, because it contained organic substances. But in 1961, Dr. Naga suggested that the organic substances had been produced by extra-terrestrial life. He also offered evidence of fossils found within the meteorite. These fossils were large and detailed compared to the minute fossils that NASA claims as possible evidence of life in meteorite ALH84001.

As with the present case, an avalanche of criticisms quickly followed Naga's claims. Discovery is only part of science; criticism and rejection are what keep science on the road. The arguments continued for some years, but it was eventually accepted that the fossil evidence was due to earthly contamination. Ragweed pollen was shown to be one of the impostors. It was also shown that the organic content of the meteorite could have been formed by radiation in space.

The two cases are, therefore, similar to some extent, though the investigation of meteorite ALH84001 has been superior because the laboratory technology now available (the latest in high-resolution scanning electron microscopy and laser mass spectrometry) is superior to that available in 1961. The evidence offered is, therefore, more detailed, and many more specialist investigators collaborated with the analysis.

The life within the rocks on Mars, of which meteorite ALH84001 is a small sample, is supposed to have lived in cracks. On Mars, 3.6 billion years ago, according to our best scenario, water flowed on the surface and was maintained there by an adequately dense atmosphere – mainly of carbon dioxide. Water with dissolved carbon dioxide flowed through the cracks within the rocks and carbonate minerals were deposited there, this process being assisted by minute microscopic life which thrived in the cracks. The researchers think the globules of carbonate are significant because this is where the

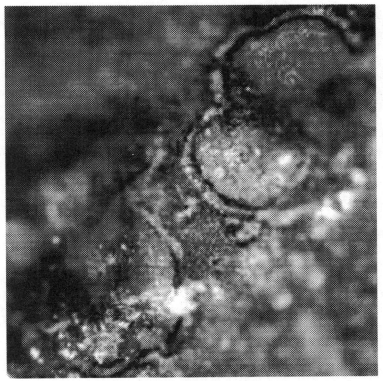

Fig. 5.2: Electron microscope image of ALH84001 sample showing carbonate grains 100-200 microns across indicative of micro-organisms (NASA photograph)

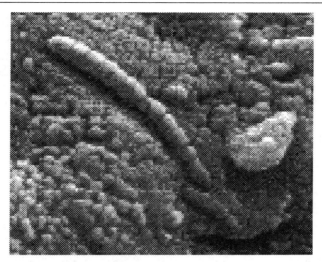

Fig. 5.3: The elongated structure, $\frac{1}{100}$th the width of a human hair, in this electron microscope image of ALH84001 may be that of a microfossil (NASA photograph).

organic molecules are concentrated, along with certain minerals which are often associated on Earth with micro-organisms – see Fig. 5.2. The fossils themselves are also there – Fig. 5.3. The fossilized state thus remained intact until 15 million years ago when a comet or large chunk of space debris hit Mars. The energy generated by this impact would have thrown many pieces of rock into space at escape velocity – that being a third for Mars compared with the Earth. Thirteen thousand years ago, one of those pieces (meteorite ALH84001) landed in Antarctica.

Professor Richard Zare of Stanford University was confident about the evidence the teams were able to offer. "It is very difficult to prove life existed 3.6 billion years ago on Earth, let alone on Mars. The existing standard proof, which we think we have met, includes having an accurately dated sample that contains native micro-fossils, mineralogical features characteristic of life, and evidence of complex organic chemistry."

That may be so, but on Earth you can hunt around for appropriate rocks – you don't have to wait for the next meteorite to arrive from Mars, or hope that the first sample-return vehicle, which is scheduled to land on Mars in 2005, will manage to pick up and return the rocks you need for confirmation.

David McKay of NASA's Johnson Space Center stressed the signifi-cance of accumulative evidence. "There is not any one finding that leads us to believe that this is evidence of past life on Mars. Rather, it is a combination of many things that we have found. They include Stanford's detection of an apparently unique pattern of organic molecules, carbon compounds that are the basis of life. We also found several unusual mineral phases that are known products of primitive microscopic organisms on Earth. Structures that could be microscopic fossils seem to support all of this. The relationship of all of these things in terms of location – within a few hundred thousandths of an inch of one another – is the most compelling evidence." Of particular importance were the range of complex organic molecules within the carbonate globules, and the iron sulphides and magnetite which, on Earth, are produced by anaerobic bacteria. (Anaerobic bacteria live only in the absence of free oxygen.) The NASA scientists also claimed that the tiny grains of magnetite are "almost identical" to the magnetic remnants sometimes found associated with fossilized bacteria on Earth. This does not look like a helpful discovery. Bacteria on Earth use magnetite to orient themselves in relation to the Earth's magnetic field. Mars doesn't have a magnetic field.

One major obstacle to the fossils being genuine is their size. The ovoids and rod-shaped objects, the fossilized Martians, range in size from a hundredth to a thousandth the diameter of a human hair. Under the electron microscope they may look like the tiniest of bacteria – but are they?

William Schopf, Professor of palaeobiology at the University of California and one of the world's leading authorities on the fossils of bacteria, was sceptical. "One is coming near to the limit in size needed to accommodate the genetic material of living systems." The Martian fossils also show no signs at all of a cell wall or internal structures.

However, microbiologist Todd Stevens, of the Pacific Northwest Laboratory, Washington, claims to have discovered live bacteria only twice the size of the meteorite Martians in fractures within rocks beneath Washington's Columbia River. Todd believes that chemical reactions between water and the rocks produce hydrogen which the bacteria use with carbon dioxide to make methane, this being their basic chemical activity from which they obtain energy to live.

Geologist Robert Folk of the University of Texas Austin, has also defended the small size of the Martian fossils. In hot springs in Italy he found bacteria of about the same size as the meteorite Martians. He also found bacterial fossils, some 2 billion years old, which are similar to the objects in ALH84001.

But all this is far from conclusive proof, as Everett Gibson of

NASA's Johnson Space Center is willing to accept. "We don't claim that we have conclusively proven it. We are putting this evidence out to the scientific community for other investigators to verify, enhance, attack – disprove if they can – as part of the scientific process." This could take several years. A firm conclusion, accepted through science, can hardly come before a comparison can be made with other Martian material, and that means waiting until a Mars Surveyor spacecraft recovers samples and returns them to Earth orbit, probably in 2005. But if life ever did flourish on Mars, there will be no shortage of fossils. There was either abundant life there or none at all, according to what we currently know about biology. If micro-organisms evolved on Mars, they will have left fossils all over the planet. There will be no doubt about the reality or not of those ancient Martians once we get to the red planet.

Thus, the question, "Does life exist elsewhere within the Solar System?" which has frustrated us for years, still remains. Until NASA's spacecraft reached Mars in the 1960s and early 1970s, most of us looked to Mars to offer a few Martians. We didn't expect advanced animals or plants, just simple and durable organisms suited to the harsh conditions we knew to exist on the planet. They would have been the survivors of a sparse evolutionary biology which had its origin a few billion years ago when life first appeared on Earth. But NASA's spacecraft told us that the atmospheric pressure was far too low for liquid water or any life to exist on the planet's surface. Everyone had to accept that there were no sizeable organisms wandering about on the surface. With practically no atmosphere, and, therefore, no atmospheric pressure, water would boil away in an instant, including the water of living things – and most living things that we know of, including ourselves, are composed more of water than anything else.

Yet those people who wanted to have a few live Martians of some sort didn't give up. They speculated that because bacteria are incredibly hardy organisms on Earth, perhaps their equivalent on Mars were even hardier. Perhaps Martian bacteria, encased in watertight membranes, were still living in protected niches on the planet. Then, in 1976, NASA's Viking Landers checked the top few inches of the Martian surface for the chemical activities of life. There were no indications of living processes at work. The media then took up the tale and began to convince everyone that Mars was sterile. I'll quote the caption of a photograph which showed the sampling arm of one of the Viking Landers, with the barren red sand and rocks of Mars in the background. The caption read: "A NASA craft took this photo of Mars in 1976. Such missions have shown that no extraterrestrial life exists in the Solar System." What the Viking Landers actually confirmed was that no life exists in the top few inches of the Martian surface in two tiny areas of Mars. It was the measurements of the very low atmospheric pressure at the planet's surface which have been all-important in convincing everybody that the existence of any surface life on Mars today is highly unlikely. That doesn't, of course, rule out the existence of fossils of micro-organisms which thrived on Mars when there existed a far denser atmosphere and, therefore, a much higher atmospheric pressure. Consequently, those scientists who were not going to give up on the possibility that Martians of some sort existed, started to devise ways of bringing back sedimentary rocks that might contain those fossils. For the task of analysing Martian life and comparing it with Earthly life, fossils are much better than sterile rocks, but not perfect. But then some startling and unforeseen discoveries were made on Earth.

The last hope for Live Martians

Our expectations of finding Martians at home, alive and well, have been almost restored by the recent discoveries of live anaerobic bacteria (bacteria which live only in the absence of free oxygen) deep beneath the Earth's surface. It has therefore become a possibility that similar organisms survive deep in the Martian crust. In retrospect, it is not surprising that the two Viking Landers, which searched only inches into the surface sand, found no evidence of life. To do the job properly, future searches will have to use the equivalent of oil-drilling technology. The fact is that anaerobic bacteria live in abundance up to several kilometres beneath the Earth's surface, where temperatures and chemical conditions are apparently ideal for them. So why shouldn't an equivalent life-form live in a similar environment on Mars? The Earth's subterranean bacteria may have been living where they are since soon after the origin of life, or, possibly, life had its origin in such a protected environment and later moved to the surface of our planet. We therefore have yet another possible site for the origin of life.

The research which has led us to consider this intriguing possibility should be examined. It was Sir James Jeans, an eminent British physicist of the inter-war years, who used to point out that science was like a great river which sometimes turned back on itself, making what today we would call a "U" turn. The latest discoveries which may tell us something about the origin of life have not yet taken us right round the bend, but the river is flowing in that direction. Our thinking about life elsewhere in the Solar System has certainly been changed in recent years. We can no longer be so sure that the Earth is its only abode.

I believe this change began with Professor Thomas Gold of Cornell University, who has long held unconventional views about the formation of natural hydrocarbons, which are our sources of oil and gas. The conventional view, the one long held by geologists, is that millions of years ago decayed trees and other vegetation were covered by succeeding layers of sediments, beneath which the vegetation was eventually transformed into oil and gas in the Earth's crust. Thomas Gold has pointed out that if oil and gas always formed in this way, they should always be beneath sedimentary rocks, but this is not so. In Sweden, Gold and his colleagues discovered all the signs that oil existed deep beneath a granite crust, and granite is not a sedimentary rock. It was never formed under water from layers of sediments. In less than a year, an American company had drilled to a depth of 6.7 kilometres and a core sample, in 30 feet of pipe, was brought to the surface.

"It had an extremely strong odour," Gold said. "You don't expect to drill deep into granite and find something with a strong and objectionable smell." The sample contained oil and fine-ground magnetite, a form of iron ore. It also contained bacteria which can live only in habitats where free oxygen is absent (anaerobic bacteria). These bacteria would have been obtaining their "food" by interacting chemically with their environment. Professor Gold also found that similar bacteria were extracted from less deep bore-holes in the United States; and they have been collected from sea vents where gas and matter are bursting through the sea bed, providing a high temperature environment for highly specialised, heat-loving bacteria.

Life in French oil?

While Gold was working in Sweden, French scientists working for Sanofi Elf Bio Researchers, a research branch of the giant oil company Elf, were recovering live bacteria of different kinds, some previously unknown, from bore holes in various parts of Africa. Dr. Michel Magot, in a letter to me about their findings, said, "We have no direct proof concerning the true origin of these bacteria, but we studied them in culture in the laboratory and they can be assumed to be indigenous to the ecosystems they came from. They live within the water aquifers in contact with the oil deposits which flood through the porous rocks. And bacterial strains from regions down to the Jurassic geological level were isolated and cultivated in the laboratory."

Michel Magot appreciates that the origin of these bacteria is crucial. "We don't think they could have migrated from the surface very recently. All the bacterial types we have isolated, sometimes in direct association with biodegraded oils, can grow only under strictly anaerobic conditions. If they had invaded their habitats from the surface – been transported there by downward flowing water – we would have found aerobic bacteria (oxygen-using bacteria), or at least facultative anaerobic bacteria." (Facultative anaerobic bacteria are bacteria which can live both with free oxygen and without it.)

"Many of the bacteria we found must be classified as new species, or even new genera," added Magot. "The evidence, therefore, indicates that they could have been evolving in completely closed ecosystems for a long time."

Our question here must be: for how long? Have they lived deep in the Earth's crust since the dawn of life? Did life first form deep underground, protected from destructive radiation and other physical hazards on the surface of the primordial Earth, and then migrate to the surface to evolve into all the life-forms, microbes and fungi, plants and animals which currently exist?

It is the molecular biology of these bacteria which may provide an answer. The French scientists have isolated several samples from bore holes where temperatures were not far short of 100 degrees C. These bacteria were similar to, but different strains of, a well studied branch of bacteria known as the thermotogales which inhabit hot springs and hot submarine vents. According to the RNA sequences of this branch of the bacterial kingdom, its members form the most ancient group of bacteria.

Does this tell us anything about the origin of life? Some scientists in this discipline maintain that the first life-forms had their origin some 4 billion years ago in such ecosystems as thermal vents. Certainly, biologists have been greatly surprised by the discovery that some bacteria thrive in the very high temperatures around marine thermal vents. Bacteria live there in temperatures higher than 100 degrees C, which would immediately destroy most other forms of life. It is still not understood why the organic substances of these heat-loving bacteria do not break down in such heat. However, the French scientists have not found any bacteria living in bore holes where the temperature is higher than 100 degrees C. That seems to be the threshold for bacteria in the Earth's crust. The rule is the deeper the bore hole, the higher the temperature and the fewer the number of bacterial strains.

The French scientists, and others in this new line of research, are extending our view of life with their discoveries, and expanding our view of what kinds of environment might support life elsewhere within the Solar System. "Our research teams push deeper and deeper under ground the limits of life," said Michel Margot. The French scientists reported collectively in a research paper, "These new biological results could constitute a further milestone in the research into the origins of life."

So both Professor Gold and the Elf scientists have independently come to the same conclusion. Another group of scientists from Bristol and Exeter Universities have also been independently pursuing this line of investigation, drilling into the sea bed in various places and classifying the bacteria present, although they have not drilled deeper than 800 meters into the crust.

Martian Microbes

These discoveries extend the known biosphere of Earth, and are relevant to our thinking about the origin of life both here and on other worlds. Yet we have to admit that the discovery of fossils of Martian microbes in ancient sedimentary rocks seems more probable than living microbes deep in the crust of Mars. The fossils, if they exist, will do so in abundance in the ancient sedimentary rocks of the planet. They could be found with space technology that is currently being built and would confirm the recent claim that Martian microbes have been associated with meteorite ALH84001 – presumably about 3.6 billion years ago. But it will be a long time before anyone can drill several kilometres into Mars in the search for living microbes.

So, how do we search for the fossils on the Martian surface? It's like searching for fossils on Earth. You need to understand the geology to be successful. Jack Farmer, a palaeontologist working at the SETI Institute in California, and Dave Desmarais, a geochemist at NASA's Ames Research Center, have collaborated to find the best places to look. They believe that the earliest bacteria on Earth were best fossilized where water existed over a long period and where precipitating minerals buried the bacteria alive. Present-day hot springs and alkaline lakes provide that sort of environment. Apparently, the photographs of Mars show several dozen sites which could be the remains of similar environments on Mars. However, better photographs are needed to aid this research before the planned robot rovers, with the technology to send samples back to Earth orbit, are landed on the planet.

Freak Event or Universal Phenomenon?

The origin of life, as a subject of research, is directly related to SETI. If it were a freak event, or a highly improbable event, then there would be little point in searching for evidence of other civilizations. Thus, the discovery of life elsewhere in the Solar System, no matter at what level, would confirm the basis of the SETI rationale that life is a universal phenomenon. The probability of life elsewhere in the Solar System, in the crust of Mars or in warm seas beneath the thick icy crust of Europa, does, however, depend on how life had its origins here. The more we understand about the origin of life here, the better our guesses should be about life elsewhere. Did life descend into the Earth after evolving in warm, organically rich seas, where the energy that put the necessary molecules together came from solar radiation or energy in some other form such as lightning? Or did life start in the Earth's crust and move up to the surface?

Professor Gold favours the second scenario. "I think the best circumstances for the first steps in the evolution of life would be extremely stable conditions with a constant temperature for long periods of time, a constant supply of energy from 'food' that could be used, and freedom from damaging radiation. All these can be had deep beneath the earth."

Gold's research and hypothesis has, therefore, changed our thinking about the possibility of finding life-forms on some of our neighbouring worlds. The space-age study of the planets and moons has, until recently, provided depressing news for biologists. Venus is much too hot for life. The low atmospheric pressure on Mars makes life on its surface impossible. The Moon is a sterile ball of rock. Now we can at least drill deep into Mars, and penetrate the think icy covering of Europa in search of life.

Future Possibilities

Life on Earth provides plenty of work for biologists, who generally don't worry much about life elsewhere. We can't, however, expect to see what is possible for life from only one example. In a way our biosphere is like one organism. Every living thing within it works in the same way and interacts, either directly or indirectly, with every other living thing. The merest microbe from another world, where life and its origin were in total isolation from our biosphere, could therefore provide a library of new biological knowledge.

The best evidence of life on Mars that could be hoped for before Gold's hypothesis was fossilised bacteria, or the Martian equivalent. But even extraterrestrial fossils of microbes would be the discovery of the century. The status of life in the universe would be extended*. Thomas Gold suggests that if life did form in the Martian crust some 4 billion years ago, as it may have done on Earth at about the same time, then that life may still flourish. Live Martians would certainly be better than fossilized Martians. They would reveal so much more about the phenomenon of life. Biologists would be able to compare the molecular structures and machinery of our life, especially the genetic code and our use of amino acid molecules to build proteins, with the ways in which life operates on another world. The genetic code which all life on Earth uses, and which confirms just one common origin for all existing life-forms, would have been already established in those bacteria of 3.5 billion years ago which we can see in the fossil record. Our genetic code is far too complicated to have evolved independently on two isolated planets, and for two neighbouring planets it would definitely be impossible. Therefore, if microbes were discovered within the Martian crust and they possessed our genetic code, then their ancestors would have had to have come from Earth, or our life would have had its origin on Mars. They would have to have a very different genetic code, and differ in other fundamental molecular ways, to confirm an independent origin of life on Mars.

---

* We do not yet know if NASA's study of meteorite ALH provides evidence of Martian fossils. It would seem that their findings can only be confirmed, or otherwise, by future investigations of the rock samples from Mars. A Surveyor spacecraft is scheduled to return samples to Earth in 2005. If their work is confirmed, the NASA scientists could justly claim the discovery of the century. But the discovery of live Martians, even the most minute micro-organism, would be far more important.

However, if life on Mars were different in its basic molecular structures from life here, we would have to assume separate origins. The conclusion would then be that life is, indeed, a universal phenomenon, which will arise anywhere in the universe where conditions make it possible, although it would use the universal chemistry available to it in its own way. The main aspects of life on Earth, such as the genetic code and its use of certain amino acids to form proteins, which are incredibly complicated processes, can never be identical in any two isolated planetary biospheres. The exploration of Mars during the next few of decades might, therefore, answer our most fundamental question and give a great boost to SETI.

If it were discovered that life had formed independently on two neighbouring worlds, Earth and Mars, so soon after their formation, it would confirm that life is a universal phenomenon and part of the great scheme of things. Providing, of course, that the molecular basis of that life was not identical to ours. If that were the case, it would indicate possible contamination. We know that the impact of very large meteorites in the past would have produced enough energy to eject fragments of the Earth and Mars into space, but whether or not microbes could survive in such fragments for many millions of years before they collided with a neighbouring world we cannot say. Contamination in this way does not look likely, but any Martian life would have to show definite differences at a molecular level from life here in order to answer the question, "Is life a universal phenomenon?"

The problem is that the rocks which the Apollo astronauts brought back from the Moon are not the only lunar rocks to land on Earth. Geologists have found numerous meteorites on the snow and ice of Antarctica which are definitely lunar rocks. The first was identified in 1982, since when others have been found. Antarctica is an ideal place to find meteorites because movements deep in the Antarctic snow and ice eventually bring meteorites to the surface, and the process by which they landed in Antarctica, and in all other parts of the world, has been going on since the early days of the Solar System. Geologists reckon that about ten small pieces of the Moon fall on the Earth every year.

We can all see from NASA's wonderful photographs that the planets and moons have taken a terrible battering. With time the scars have been covered up on Earth, but not so on the Moon and elsewhere. Meteorites have often hit the Moon with enough force to send bits of the lunar surface flying into space. Most of the debris falls back onto the Moon, but some pieces have enough energy to escape into elliptical lunar orbits. Some pieces, as their orbits take them close to the Moon, will be thrown further into space by its gravity. A proportion will eventually take up orbits which cross the orbit of the Earth, putting them on a potential collision course with us.

The discovery and identification of small lunar rocks on the snow of Antarctica has, therefore, led geologists and astronomers to recognise a mechanism for the exchange of material between the planets and moons. It was an idea that was not taken too seriously until the early 1980s, but what is it to do with SETI? It will, in fact, change our approach to any microbes that might be found deep under the surface of Mars or in any other highly protected niche on that planet. We have now accepted the reality of the process by which lunar rocks have been blasted into space since the Moon existed, and it is almost certain that this also applies to the rocky planets. There is no shortage of impact craters on Mars, and, with the aid of photography from space, we can still see evidence of some immense craters on the Earth. What seems conclusive evidence is that geologists have identified several meteorites as coming from Mars, and these include meteorite ALH84001 which may be showing evidence of very ancient Martians. Though not until NASA is able to recover samples directly from the red planet can the possible evidence of life in this meteorite be confirmed.

Jay Melosh, a professor of planetary science at the Lunar and Planetary Laboratory at the University of Arizona, is one of the scientists studying the meteorites from the Moon and Mars. "We are reasonably certain that a group of nine meteorites, the so-called SNCs (for Shergotty, Nakhla and Chassigny, named after the sites where they landed), originated on the planet Mars." Not surprisingly, no one saw any of the meteorites from the Moon fall on Antarctica, but four of the nine pieces of Mars have actually been witnessed falling to Earth. "In 1911," says Melosh, "a piece of Nakhla, which fell near Alexandria, Egypt, killed a dog, scoring the only known fatality (of a mammal) caused by a meteorite."

This whole situation is somewhat ironic. Since the possibility arrived of sending probes and astronauts to the Moon and Mars, everyone looked forward with anticipation to retrieving sample rocks from these worlds, not knowing that samples have been falling on the Earth for billions of years. "The total of Martian material falling onto Earth has been estimated at about half a ton a year," says Melosh.

Transferring rocks from one world to another is one thing. Transferring life in the form of microbes is another. First, could life survive the impact of a large meteorite? Rock directly beneath the impact will receive enough energy to melt and vapourise it, but surface rocks very close to the impact will not be so affected. "However," says Melosh, "the pressure increases very rapidly with depth below the surface, which translates into a powerful acceleration that throws lightly shocked surface rocks out at speeds comparable to the original speed of the impactor." Research at the Lawrence Livermore Laboratory, in which aluminium projectiles were fired at granite blocks at speeds of about four kilometres a second, showed this to be correct. Tiny pieces of the granite were blasted off at speeds of around 1 kilometre a second and caught in foam. These millimetre-sized fragments were then found to be only lightly shocked. Thus it looks as if surface rocks could be ejected from the Moon or Mars or Earth in a condition that would enable any microbes within to survive. But that would be only the start of their journey. Could they survive hundreds of thousands to hundreds of millions of years in space before a collision orbit took them to another world? It seems unlikely but we do not know.

They might be adequately protected from radiation within large chunks of rock – bacteria can certainly survive the vacuum of space. They have the capacity to freeze dry themselves in such conditions. Microbiologists store bacteria in vacuum containers, and bacteria recovered from the camera system of Surveyor 3, after several years on the Moon, were restored to normal bacterial activity. Some scientists have also claimed to have revived bacteria from geologic deposits: from a few million years old, in the case of Siberian permafrost, up to a couple of hundred million years in ancient salt beds. The evidence for the survival of bacteria beyond about three million years is not, however, widely accepted.

From the viewpoint of SETI, we have to consider two more questions because we know that life must have been present on Earth about four billion years ago. At that time, because conditions on Mars may have been similar to those on Earth, there is the possibility that life also formed on Mars, as research on meteorite ALH84001 may be showing. Coinciding with the origin of life, all the planetary bodies were under intense bombardment from a great deal of rocky debris, the remains of which still pervades interplanetary space. One only has to look at the Moon, including photographs of its far side which we never see from Earth, to realise how great that bombardment must have been. It was, therefore, much easier when life was first emerging for Martian rocks to reach the Earth and for fragments of the Earth to have reached Mars.

I wouldn't want to speculate that life originated on Mars and then came to Earth in a piece of rock. Conditions for the origin of life would almost certainly have been better on Earth. Nevertheless, we could speculate that rocks with the first bacteria may have been blasted to Mars by the impacts of large meteorites on Earth. This is a possibility that biologists will have to consider if they are ever in a position to examine the Martian equivalent of live bacteria which might exist deep beneath the surface of Mars. The worldwide phenomenon of bacteria living up to six kilometres beneath the Earth's surface, obtaining their sustenance from chemically reacting with their sub-terranean environment, makes this a possibility.

Therefore, if biologists are ever in the epoch-making position of comparing our microbes with some from Mars, they would be looking for similarities and differences at a fundamental level – at a molecular and genetic level. A molecular basis for Martian life that was different from ours would indicate that life there had an independent origin, and a subsequent evolution in complete isolation. Similarities at the molecular level, of the specific amino acid molecules used to make proteins and the molecular machinery of the genetic code, could indicate an exchange of life between the Earth and Mars in the distant past. We need not, of course, stop with Mars. There is the remote possibility of life within the warm water beneath the thick ice crust of Europa. Could rocks from Earth have crashed through that ice eons ago? The impacts of large meteorites, by blasting rocks into space, might have spread life to any world with a niche to sustain it. It's unlikely, but, from what we know at present, not impossible.

Jay Melosh has given the example of rocks up to a metre across being blasted long distances by meteorite impacts. Blocks from the top layer of limestone which surround the Ries crater in Germany were discovered, relatively little damaged, in Switzerland. They had been thrown a distance of almost 200 kilometres. There have been far greater impacts in the past. While the Ries crater is only 24 kilometres across, the crater in Yucantán, which is thought to have been produced by the meteorite which put an end to the dinosaurs 65 million years ago, has a diameter of 180 kilometres.

There have been equally large impacts by meteorites at earlier times in Earth history. It would have been the really early strikes that might have transported life to Mars, and many massive meteorites were still colliding with the inner planets and the Moon for millions of years after the origin of life on Earth about 4 billion years ago. This would have been the best time for Mars to have received bacterial visitors from Earth. Conditions there were probably more Earth-like in those days so that any infection by our bacteria might have migrated deep within the Martian crust as Mars lost its atmosphere and surface water, and conditions on the surface became too harsh for even bacteria to tolerate. But this is speculation. We cannot know until Mars is investigated, including deep drillings to obtain cores from kilometres beneath the surface.

Jay Melosh contemplates what is a possible, but an unanticipated situation. "Given the possibility of exchange of life among the planets by large impacts, we may have to regard the terrestrial planets not as biologically isolated, but rather as a single ecological system with components, like islands in the sea, that occasionally communicate with one another."

Chapter Six

The Immortal Network

The idea behind the Immortal Network is simple: it provides a mind for the whole universe for all time. Once it has grown to maturity and it may have done so a billion years ago, it could provide civilizations within numerous galaxies with whatever information they might wish to seek. Civilizations which have discovered the Immortal Network could plug into it permanently. They could then receive a constant flow of information on everything of interest that has taken place since the first technological beings, with an innate desire to communicate with their counterparts amongst the stars, started the system. The beauty of the Immortal Network would be that distance would make little difference once the system was established. Given that the Network's terminals were, say, a few hundred light-years apart, a civilization could as easily learn about life in neighbouring galaxies as life on planets in orbit about neighbouring stars. It could take hundreds of years for our questions to be answered, which for a short-lived species like ourselves would be somewhat frustrating, but there might be a constant transmission of information, which we might receive immediately and permanently.

This kind of scenario is the dream which drives those in astronomical SETI. We cannot know at present if it is possible to cross interstellar space, even given the ultimate in spacecraft technology. The speed-of-light limitation may forever prevent journeys to distant worlds. If these barriers imposed upon us by the nature of the universe cannot be overcome, then the Immortal Network would appear to be the solution for all ETs who, like ourselves, have a deep desire to know what our counterparts on other worlds have done in the past. Civilizations in neighbouring galaxies which sent information about their cultures across the light-years many millions of years ago, civilizations which may no longer even exist, could have registered their existence and achievements on the Immmortal Network.

It would be an ideal arrangement for intelligence everywhere, though it would not preclude our counterparts with the appropriate space technology from coming to the Solar System to explore and study our world, if that was also a feasible option.

The detection of evidence of ET's presence in the Solar System, either in the past or in the present, would certainly confirm the hypothesis that life is a universal phenomenon, but such a discovery, or discoveries, might not give us information about our visitors and their worlds, unless they wished us to have such information. On the other hand, a data bank on the Moon or Mars might have been left long ago by visiting ETs, if such visits were rare and difficult. If they were unlikely to return, they might have left some record of themselves. We have already done precisely this with the Pioneer and Voyager spacecraft which will carry evidence of us and the Earth across interstellar space for millions of years. A data bank might not be a continuous and permanent source of information, whereas the Immortal Network, if the radio astronomers in SETI can find the nearest terminal, could be just that.

A free flow of information across the light-years would change many worlds and many ways of life. It would be something like our emerging Internet, though carrying billions of times more information. The Internet was an inevitable development, given the way in which computer science and technology has developed. Perhaps the Immortal Network was just as inevitable when the technology for its establishment became available, given, of course, that life and intelligence are abundant throughout the universe.

Broadcasts from other Worlds

We have already considered the possible height of ceilings to knowledge in the universe. How much there is for scientists to discover and technologists to apply we do not know, but on the answer to this question will depend the level of future technologies. If the nature of the universe can provide scientists with a virtually unlimited supply of new fundamental information about the universe, then a wonderful range of new technologies would be developed on the basis of this. If the ceiling to major fundamental knowledge is low, and we reach that ceiling in approximately a century or so, then nobody will be going to the stars and our communications will be limited to the speed of light. The scientific understanding for the development of both space vehicles which could cross the light-years and faster-than-light communications may not exist – anywhere, at any time.

In such a situation, the only possible contact between worlds would be by radio or some other section of the electromagnetic spectrum. The lower the ceiling to knowledge, therefore, the greater the chances the astronomers have of discovering evidence of ETs, and the greater the possibility that ET messages could be understood eventually. Indeed, unless the ceilings are very low, we may never be able to do more than just detect the presence of advanced ETs. Communications may be impossible.

Nevertheless, our hypothesis in this book is that ET activity may be abundant enough, and varied enough, for evidence of it to be detectable. Thus, our initial concern is the detection of this evidence, which would confirm the hypothesis that life and intelligence are universal phenomena. For the present, any understanding of intelligent signals, if we could understand them, is of secondary importance (see Fig. 6.1).

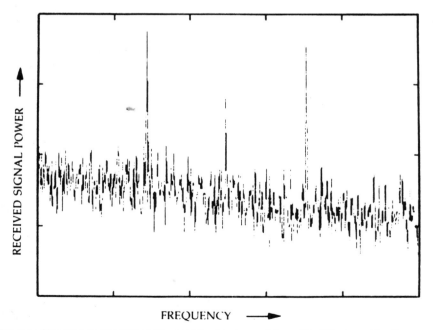

Fig. 6.1: Signal transmitted from Pioneer 10 when beyond the orbit of Neptune. The three components stand out clearly from the background noise. Signals from another world might be this evident or be very difficult to distinguish from background radiation.

Since Project Ozma in 1960, when Professor Frank Drake carried out the first search for evidence of ET, astronomers have made more than 50 searches. These have lasted from a few hours to several years, and some major searches have been continuous. Drake used the 85-feet radio telescope at the United States National Radio Observatory at Green Bank, West Virginia, to study two nearby stars, Tau Ceti and Epsilon Eridani. He observed them for 200 hours on the universal hydrogen line at 1.4 GHz during a period of three months, using only a single-channel receiver. In retrospect we can see that his failure to find ET was inevitable, but he started the world thinking about the subject.

In 1995, at the opening ceremony for the SETI receiver system called BETA (the most powerful in the world, which astronomers at Harvard University are using), Frank Drake said that it is a trillion times more powerful than his Project Ozma in 1960. Revolutionary developments in electronics and computer technology have made such an advance possible. Paul Horowitz, a physics professor, has run a continuous SETI programme at Harvard University since 1983, supported by the Planetary Society, the largest society of its kind in the world. The astronomers, who use the Harvard-Smithsonian Observatory, have advanced from using a system called META, which scanned more than eight million channels simultaneously, to the present BETA system (the Billion-channel Extraterrestrial Assay) which continuously monitors the so-called water hole band of frequencies from 1,400 to 1,720 MHz. This is part of the quietest band of frequencies crossing space which reaches the Earth's surface. The other part of this band does not penetrate the atmosphere, and will have to wait until radio dishes for SETI can be placed in orbit. But BETA is a great advance, being able to monitor the equivalent of 2 billion radio channels. It can do more in a second than Frank Drake in 1960 was able to do in three months.

Horowitz and his colleagues observe the entire northern sky in six months. The telescope, fixed in position while the Earth turns on its axis, sweeps the sky with one beam width of the telescope each day. Since the Earth is turning, a signal would be in the beam for about two-and-a-half minutes, and interesting signals are stored for later examination.

Despite the difficulties, Paul Horowitz is confident (which he needs to be to persist in such a difficult endeavour). "I believe the odds on there being advanced civilizations in our Milky Way galaxy are a thousand to one on. Every day we pick up radio noise from space that is equal to 22 trillion bytes of data, equivalent in information content to 50 million novels." One can feel confident that Horowitz will find ET's broadcasts if they are being transmitted on the frequency band which is being observed with such ingenuity and perseverance. It's hard to doubt the probability that advanced societies exist on some of the planets which orbit the several billion carbon copies of the Sun in our galaxy. The problem is guessing what they may be doing, especially as they are going to be at least thousands of years ahead of us. Within a few thousand years, if the human race prospers, the capacity and understanding of human beings is going to be vastly different from what it is today. Therefore, to base a research project on the assumption that members of advanced societies will think like us is a gamble. But the gamble doesn't cost much, and it focuses people's attention on a rich range of science which relates directly to our situation on this planet. It brings astronomy and biology together in interesting ways and generates new ideas.

In the 35 years between Drake's pioneering Project Ozma and the BETA system, there have been many ingenious developments in receivers and search strategies. During 1972-76 at Green Bank, the same observatory Drake had used, astronomers Palmer and Zuckerman monitored the hydrogen line at 1.4 GHz for 500 hours for a sign of alien intelligence on any worlds orbiting 674 Sun-like stars. The Ohio State University Radio Observatory, with its 110 by 21 metre radio telescope, is devoted to the world's longest running SETI programme. Bob Dixon, Director of the Observatory, and his many colleagues have carried out all-sky searches since 1973. Their observations have continued, more or less uninterrupted, 24 hours a day, scanning a microwave band which includes the hydrogen line. During the years they have greatly improved their receiving system as new electronics and computer technology have become available. Besides the objective of discovering an intelligent extraterrestrial signal, Bob Dixon wants to proclaim SETI as a unifying activity for all nations, and flies the Flag of Earth over the Observatory.

Like other searchers, the Ohio team has had its share of false alarms, including the best known unexplained signal, the 'Wow' signal, so-called because the telescope operator at the time wrote 'Wow' on the recording chart. The problem has been that SETI observations have had to depend on computers handling the incoming signals, since astronomers do not have the time to stand by their receivers. Over the years many interesting "Wow-type" signals have been recorded, but the astronomers have never been able to find those signals again when they turned their telescopes back to the recorded coordinates. Numerous interesting signals have thus remained unexplained – which, of course, does not mean that they came from ET. However, the systems at Ohio State University and at Harvard now automatically continue to monitor any interesting signals until they are no longer observable.

Politicians Reject ET

The NASA SETI Program, the most ambitious endeavour so far, was part of NASA's Planetary Biology Program with the fully-accepted scientific aim of understanding the origin and evolution of life in the universe. NASA took SETI into a more comprehensive, coordinated and centrally controlled level of research than had previously been attempted. The Program was begun in October 1982, under the directorship of Bernard Oliver, a SETI veteran. For several years scientists at NASA's Ames Research Center, the Jet Propulsion Laboratory and Stanford University, developed the receiving equipment, including computers and signal analysers, and a great deal of specially-written computer software, including signal recognition programs that enable the system to function most of the time without human attention. Such advances make old radio telescopes and radar dishes adequate for SETI. In 1993, however, politicians in Washington, not understanding the value of a major SETI program as a means of providing the public with a mass of interesting science, voted to end the Program. The money saved wouldn't have financed a good science fiction film. The SETI Institute in California, which had been working with NASA, finding the cheapest ways for the required research and development, then took over the Program with financial backing from numerous imaginative companies and individuals. The Program, now known as Project Phoenix, is using radio telescopes and old radar installations in several countries. A team at Stanford University had built a special signal analyser for the original NASA program. It scans eight million frequencies simultaneously, and several copies of the prototype are being taken from telescope to telescope around the world. Like other SETI observations, Project Phoenix runs as automatically as possible and will continue for ten years or more.

The Lucky Chance Factor

The question of where we should look for ET's signal in the electro-magnetic spectrum is so obviously unanswerable that some scientists have decided to ignore it. Professor Stuart Bowyer and colleagues at the University of California, Berkeley, have been one group to show that it isn't really necessary to enter the guessing game. They first began to use their SERENDIP system in 1977. Bowyer's team managed to concoct this acronym from 'Search for Extraterrestrial Radio Trans-missions from Nearby Developed Intelligent Populations', since their observational technique relied on serendipity, the capacity to make desirable but unsought-for discoveries by chance.

Bowyer and colleagues developed their system for several thou-sand dollars initially, and since 1992 have been using SERENDIP III. The SERENDIPs, being transportable, can be plugged into any radio telescope without affecting the observations in progress. In other words, it piggybacks on telescopes being used for conventional radio astronomy, monitoring whatever is being received, and rejecting everything except possible signals from ET. It thus avoids a major problem for SETI: the shortage of time available on radio telescopes heavily engaged in astronomical research, even though its search strategy is random. "But it is searching somewhere, at some level of sensitivity, for extended periods of time," says Bowyer. "Searching is like turning on your radio and trying to find a station amidst all the static. We're looking for a strong narrow signal that could not be produced by anything in nature."

SERENDIP is checked out once a month, when hundreds of re-corded signals have to be explained. Most are from intelligent activi-ties on this planet, or from faults in the receiver, but the system has been improved to cut down on the false alarms.

Guessing about ETs

The kind of signal for which radio astronomers search depends upon what they think ETs might be transmitting. The great difficulty here is that radio astronomy is a very young science and the transmitting ET civilizations, if they exist, are going to be very old. Our best bet is to assume that we are about average: that many species of technologi-cal creatures have evolved somewhat like ourselves, though probably on widely differing time-scales. We may be correct in this assump-tion, or hopelessly wrong. We may never know which, but we have to assume something to form any hypothesis that can be tested. Admittedly, the favoured frequencies already scanned have carried no intelligent signal, but the search has only just begun. The range of possible frequencies used by ET is vast, and the Galaxy a rather large volume of space to search.

We accept that the evolution of technological species must produce curious, communicative, exploratory creatures. Therefore, we assume that for at least a period of their history our counterparts on other worlds will be motivated in ways that would be familiar to us; we do so in order to guess what they may have done. If we think that all ETs will be totally different from ourselves in their evolution and ways of thinking, then we cannot guess their probable actions. It would be impossible and there would be little point in pursuing our subject. Yet we cannot but suppose that some technological ETs will be completely different from us, either because of their very different biological histories or because they have advanced far beyond our present stage of development.

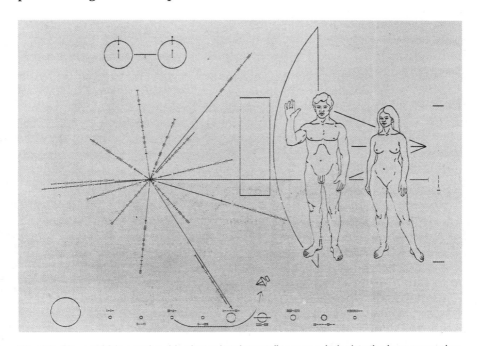

Fig. 6.2: Pioneer 10 is carrying this plaque into interstellar space. It depicts the human species and provides astronomical information on the location of Earth. Other beings may have done something similar, perhaps in a more elaborate way.

We can confine our speculations to ETs that are social creatures (although not like the social insects which are automata) with an innate drive to communicate. They may attempt to communicate to other worlds only in monologue, if they know that dialogue is not possible. A one-way communication between worlds is probably better than no communication at all. They may want to register their history in eternity. We have already done much the same thing with our messages on the Pioneer and Voyager spacecraft, although no one anywhere is likely to discover these first messages of ours (see Fig. 6.2). Nevertheless, they do proclaim that we were once here, orbiting a star whose location is given in our message, along with the records of some of our best achievements. These craft are sure to journey undetected through interstellar space for millions of years, but ETs, with more practice in space age technology, may be more effective in conveying their messages to other worlds.

If we are looking for dialogue, we can ignore the possible existence of ETs which are totally different from ourselves and those which have advanced beyond our comprehension, though we could conceivably detect evidence of such beings. Without very low ceilings to knowledge and technology in this universe, to which the average civilization could rise in a few hundred years from our present level, there could be hundreds of extraterrestrial civilizations for every one that we could comprehend. The gaps in comprehension could be unbridgeable. An ET which is no more beyond us than we are beyond our nearest living relative, the chimpanzee, might not be able to communicate with us across interstellar distances, even if it wanted to.

Understanding ET's Data Bank

Let us imagine an even closer contact. Suppose some scholars of the Roman Empire of 2,000 years ago discover a modern library of science and technology which has conveniently slipped back into their time. These Roman scholars are as intelligent as anyone today, although possessing information and attitudes different from ourselves. They do, however, possess a good deal of history and culture in common with ourselves. The gulf between the scholars and the library is just 2,000 years of human history. Given that they could master our language, how long would it take them to understand modern science and apply its information? My guess would be at least several generations.

Contrast their problems with the problems unknown to us of similar people (ourselves) who may find an alien data bank, say, on the Moon. We might be separated from the creators of the data bank not by 2,000 years, but by two million or even two billion years. We are also not only a different species, but of a different evolutionary biology. We may anticipate that our problems would be vastly greater than those of our Roman scholars. Only universal ceilings to knowledge and intelligence that are very low would make it possible for us ever to comprehend the contents of such a data bank.

The Ultimate System

Radio astronomers involved in SETI have defined an advanced technological civilization as 'one having advanced radio techniques'. Admittedly, all advanced technological civilizations may have used radio techniques, but would they continue to use them? That is the question. Will our major means of communication of the twentieth century be the major communications technology of advanced civilizations in the universe? That question also asks if radio is the ultimate technology for interstellar communications.

We know already that although a 'speed of light' system is highly satisfactory on Earth, it becomes less so for even relatively short distances within the Solar System. The unavoidable time-lag in communicating with the computers aboard distant unmanned spacecraft, such as those surveying the outer planets and their moons, is already beginning to present problems. A hundred years ago, there were no radio communications on Earth. It was only in 1888 that the German physicist Heinrich Hertz discovered radio waves, and only in 1901 that Guglielmo Marconi transmitted the first message by radio waves across the Atlantic. So are we very bold or very naïve in thinking that civilizations that could have preceded us by millions of years will still be communicating by radio, although employing considerably more power to do so? Perhaps we are like the natives of Papua-New Guinea who used drums to send their messages, and who thought that more advanced people would communicate across the seas by using larger drums? Or are we like some of the North American Indians who, accustomed to sending smoke signals, thought that smoke rising to the skies from great fires would enable them to communicate with distant lands?

Those radio astronomers who search for ET's radio communications are assuming one of two things: either that no new physics will be discovered that could lead to a more effective communications technology, or that some ETs will use radio frequencies, quite possibly an obsolete method to them. It could be that we already have all the fundamental information the universe can offer for interstellar communications. In this case, we can count on most communicating ETs having reached the limit of technical perfectibility in radio. If radio is the universal ultimate in interstellar communications, limited as it would be to the speed of light, there may be little two-way communication in the Galaxy, unless widespread colonization has brought ET civilizations within a few light-years of each other. Many ETs could then be living in planetary systems to which they had migrated, in systems where no Earth-like planets ever existed or could have evolved. The 'speed of light' limitation of electromagnetic radiation would even then be a severe frustration, but a 'waiting time' of a decade or two might be tolerable. Such a situation, although nearly ideal for interstellar communications, implies widespread interstellar travel. ETs might in this case prefer to come and discover Earth for themselves, rather than sending messages to its inhabitants. Alternatively, if thousands of light-years separate ETs and everyone is limited to speed-of-light communications, the Immortal Network may be the best we can hope to find. We then have to rely on wise and benevolent ETs having set up such a communications system many millions of years ago. Even if no networks exist, some advanced civilizations may still be beaming their messages across the Galaxy without any expectation of ever receiving a reply. Of course, if the laws of nature allow faster than light communications, we cannot expect super civilizations to wait any longer than they have to for replies to their celestial messages. If communications at a speed vastly greater than the 'speed of light' are possible, then it might not matter how far apart communicating ETs are, and flourishing networks of information are more probable, though we would not yet know enough physics to join in the conversations.

What Frequencies?

Assuming that ET messages are being transmitted by radio or by other frequencies of the electromagnetic spectrum, the main problem is the virtually limitless number of possible frequencies in which communications may be sent. Nothing could offer a wider choice than the electromagnetic spectrum. Background noise from the universe is at a minimum between 1 and 60 GHz, so a signal within this microwave band, which can be observed from space without interference, is a probability. From beneath our atmosphere, however, this interference-free band is reduced to about 1 GHz to 10 GHz (see Fig. 6.3). Nevertheless, within this specific waveband lie the frequencies of neutral hydrogen and the hydroxyl-frequencies – both important frequencies in radio astronomy. Many people in SETI think that ETs might use such prominent frequencies because they exist in the quietest section of the electromagnetic spectrum, where the least amount of energy would be needed to transmit signals across interstellar space.

The Water Hole

Decisions about which part of the electromagnetic spectrum to search have aroused much controversy. The section which has attracted most attention is a part of the microwave band now known as the 'water hole'. At one end is the most prominent frequency of hydrogen (H), whilst at the other end is the frequency radiated by the OH combination of atoms. Put these two together (H and OH) and you have H_2O – water! Though this is only symbolic water. You can't mix hydrogen and OH (the hydroxyl radical) together and make water. However, it might not only be the symbolic significance of the "water hole" which could make ETs broadcast on these frequencies. This part of the microwave band would be economical in terms of the energy needed to broadcast.

In NASA's SETI report SP-419, Barney Oliver wrote, "Nature has provided us with a rather narrow band in the best part of the spectrum that seems especially marked for interstellar contact ... it lies between the spectral lines of hydrogen (1.4 GHz) and the hydroxyl radical (1.7 GHz). Standing like Om and Um on either side of a gate, these two emissions of the disassociation product of water beckon all water-based life to search for its kind at the age-old meeting place of all species: the water hole."

The water frequency at 22.2 GHz is also interesting. All water-based life (which may mean all life everywhere) would see the significance of the 22.2 GHz frequency of the water molecule, as they may see the significance of the "water hole". And this is a more specific part of the electromagnetic spectrum, whereas the 'water hole' does cover 300 million frequencies. The problem is that water in our atmosphere radiates at this frequency and searches would have to be made in space to escape this interference. However, astronomers

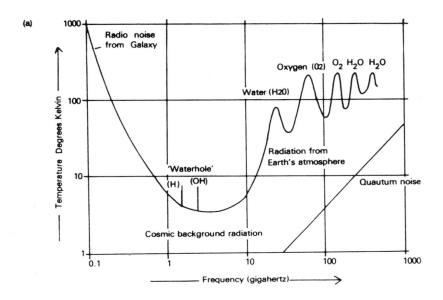

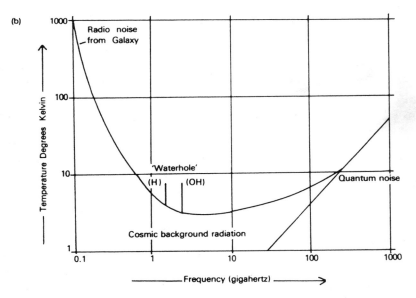

Fig. 6.3: (a) Beneath our atmosphere, the distribution of microwave radiation has a "quiet zone" betweem the radio noise (left) and quantum noise (right); (b) The microwave window from space is wider, but still limited by radio noise and quantum noise.

have monitored the water line at 22.2 GHz. from the Earth's surface. Alan Bridle and Paul Feldman at the Algonquin Radio Observatory in Canada did so from 1974 to 1976, when observing 70 Sun-like stars within 45 light-years of the Earth.

Radio astronomers and physicists not involved in SETI have studied the spectacular sources of the water frequency in the Galaxy. There are vast clouds of water and other matter surrounding newly forming stars, especially the very bright O and B stars. Energy from these stars is absorbed by the water molecules and then pumped out at the 22.2 GHz frequency by what the physicists call a maser action (short for 'Microwave Amplification by Stimulated Emission of Radiation'). A maser works like a laser, but the radiation is microwaves instead of light, hence the 'M' instead of 'L'. About 300 of these vast water masers are known in the Galaxy, and the most spectacular radiates as much energy in the 22.2 GHz frequency as the Sun does in all frequencies. Radio astronomers have also discovered water masers associated with old giant stars at the end of their life cycle. The water frequency is, therefore, a prominent characteristic of the Galaxy.

Dismayed Astronomers

Most scientists in SETI have thought that transmitting civilizations would broadcast on narrow bands containing as few frequencies as possible. They would thus be able to concentrate their available energy into a narrow channel to transmit more powerful signals. This assumption has been questioned by Frank Drake, the pioneer of observational SETI and current Director of the SETI Institute. Drake and a colleague had studied this problem when they worked together at the Arecibo Observatory. "The great expectation that extraterrestrial signals would be extremely narrow-band affected our equipment design," said Drake. "We were heading toward narrower and narrower channels in the hope of capturing the most narrow-band signals of all."

However, Drake and his colleague George Helou discovered that even single frequencies broaden into bands of frequencies as they travel through the vast clouds of electrons in interstellar space. It would, therefore, be impossible to receive ET's signals on a single frequency. Broad bands of frequencies would also be spread out by the electron clouds so that the different frequencies of a signal could arrive over a period of as much as a few minutes, depending on how far they had travelled, the highest frequencies arriving first.

Thus Drake has pointed out a major problem for the transmission of microwaves through interstellar space. Vast clouds of electrons would spread out signals over interstellar distances, but higher frequencies than that of neutral hydrogen would be less affected. This is an observable fact. "Extraterrestrials would not have to come up with theories to figure it out," said Drake.

ETs might, therefore, choose a frequency which was less affected by the electron clouds and which was also within the quietest frequency band offered by the universe (see Fig. 6.3). From these considerations, Drake has suggested what he thinks might be the optimum frequency for communications across the light-years. It works out at about 70 GHz. This is where the most easily detectable signals can be transmitted with the least consumption of energy. The temporary trouble for us is that this section of the frequency band does not penetrate the atmosphere, but it may not be many years before Drake's hypothesis can be put to the test.

Drake's Dream

Frank Drake has a recurring dream about receiving an unmistakable signal from a civilization several thousand light-years away. The signal is obviously dense with information, but there's too much noise for him to get at any of it. He accepts this scenario as a possibility and looks forward to bigger and better receivers which would enable he and his colleagues to obtain better quality signals. "On the Moon, where gravity is only one sixth that of the Earth, we could use conventional materials, steel and aluminium, to build an Arecibo-style telescope thirty miles wide. The real Arecibo is one fifth of one mile wide, so that the Moon version would be 150 times bigger in diameter, making it several thousand times larger in energy-collecting area. What faint signals such a system could detect!" The Moon would be ideal. Just pick your crater out of thousands available for the installation. But we won't see that happening for many decades – not until well-established lunar bases are operating. Unless, that is, Drake's dream becomes a reality and someone detects a first, but indistinct message from Planet-X. The rush would then be on to build Drake's telescope on the Moon.

The Call Signal

Perhaps our best chance is that a permanent provision may be made for new arrivals – for civilizations just emerging from their planetary egg, like a newborn chick. If so, a continuously transmitted 'call signal' seems the most probable evidence that we may find. What form might the 'call signal' take? We can hope that ET would make it relatively easy to detect. It's been suggested that it might contain the minimum of information to allow the receiver to plug into a more elaborate transmission – to connect with the Immortal Network, perhaps. If the call signal is sent by very advanced ETs, it may be transmitted to reach most stars in the Galaxy, so that we might expect the transmitter to be in space and its transmission not to be directed at target stars.

The laws of the universe dictate that the energy needed to transmit increases drastically with the distance at which the signal is to be received. We meet here a fundamental law of physics: the old inverse square law. The increase in power needed will be proportional to the square of the distance. Therefore, if we increase the distance from 50 to 100 light-years, we need four times more energy. Increase the distance to 1,000 light-years and we need 400 times more energy for our transmission than we did to reach out to 50 light-years. For this reason, the transmitter (or transmitters) of the 'call signal' may sweep the Galaxy with a narrow beam; the narrower the beam the less energy needed to sweep any given volume of space. We would detect such a signal as regular pulses of radiation. The length of time that we could receive a 'call signal' would depend on the relative positions of the transmitter and ourselves. Obviously, the greater the distance between us, the greater the spread of the beam and the longer the period of time the Earth would be within it, as the beam swept around the Galaxy.

Octopoid Mentality

We have to allow for the possibility that any ETs out there are either too advanced or too different from us for their broadcasts to be deciphered here. Our counterparts on another world who evolved from an octopoid life-form, instead of a particular line in fishes (which on Earth were the ancestors of all vertebrates, including ourselves), may view things rather differently from ourselves. That doesn't matter at present if we accept that SETI, in all its forms, is basically the search for evidence that life and intelligence are universal phenomena. If an intelligent signal is detected (an intelligent signal would be one that could not possibly come from a natural celestial source) then we would know that life must be universal and, therefore, part of the great scheme of things. We don't have to understand the signals to be successful in SETI. Information gathered later would be a bonus, or a liability, depending on how we applied the information. Wise ETs, knowing the possible abuse of technology, may, therefore, never transmit applicable knowledge. ETs engaged in the interstellar broadcasting business for thousands of years, having been longtime survivors and not destroyed by their own technology, would understand the danger.

Whatever ET's messages may contain, scientists plan to be ready to follow up on the first contact. Jean Heidmann, who coordinates SETI for France and the International Astronomical Union, has, with other scientists, set up The SETI Global Network. If an ET signal is detected, this network will give all SETI observers the information they would need to confirm the discovery. According to Heidmann, "The network is there to coordinate the activities of potential discoverers and has been endorsed by the International Astronomical SETI Committee and the International Astronomical Bioastronomy Commission."

Deadly Debris

One possibility which favours astronomical SETI is that interstellar space may harbour a great deal of debris. A fairly uniform distribution of dust and larger chunks of matter might make journeys to the planetary systems of other stars too dangerous for astronauts. Currently, however, most astronomers believe that the interstellar medium is benign towards spacecraft. It has been estimated that the Pioneer and Voyager spacecraft should remain more or less intact for the next billion years. These craft represent only our initial successes in the space probe business, so they must be low on the scale of durability compared to the space probes of more advanced technologies.

If, on the other hand, interstellar space could not be crossed, it would not matter a great deal how durable your spacecraft were. In this situation, astronomical SETI would be popular everywhere in the Galaxy. At present, though, we don't really know what the situation is. Numerous physical hazards, plus the time needed to cross the light-years, might encourage biological beings to stay at home and leave intelligent probes to do the exploring for them. We can speculate that their artificial intelligence would only be activated if, or when, they arrived at their target, so that they would know nothing of their existence until they arrived at distant planetary systems. What the intelligent probes might do after that is any science fiction writer's guess.

Barney Oliver, once one of the most active scientists in SETI, who died in 1996 at the age of 79, often said, "The reason they don't travel to us is that radio works so well." The only objection to this view is that we can currently have no idea whether ETs have travelled to the Solar System or not. They could have been monitoring developments on Earth for the past few hundred million years and we would know nothing about it. Nevertheless, what Barney Oliver has said is important because we don't know what the situation is. Radio does offer a good way for interstellar communications and possibly the only way in certain circumstances. There is no question that the low cost research of astronomical SETI is justified, and it has made amazing progress since the 60s, both experimentally and theoretically. The detection of messages (rather than evidence of ETs technology) is, however, uncomfortably dependent on communicating civilizations being at about the same level in intelligence and in technology at about the same time. "Listeners" for evidence of other worlds during the past few billion years, like the scientists in astronomical SETI today, would be in the same dependent position. They would depend on a constant supply of ET broadcasters since the first broadcasting civilizations evolved a few billion years ago. As we've only used our astronomical technology to listen since 1960, it's not surprising that we're still feeling our way in this subject.

The Fatal Flaw

There is a flaw in the rationale of astronomical SETI which could be fatal, as far as detecting messages for us is concerned. It seems obvious that if the possibility to explore is an option for advanced civilizations, then explore they will, rather than broadcasting messages across the light-years that no one may ever receive. Little men of every shade of green could have been broadcasting to us for the past 350 million years, since they first spotted the spectral lines of ozone and oxygen from our atmosphere. They would have known that there was a life-bearing planet here, but they wouldn't have known that its brightest inhabitants at that time were primitive amphibians. They would have had to come here, or to have sent advanced probes, to discover that there was no one around who was likely to invent radio in the foreseeable future.

However, if such direct exploration is not an option, perhaps because world civilizations are too widely separated within the Galaxy or because interstellar space contains too much debris to be crossed, then civilizations would broadcast, and, given a few million years, might have established a network which is waiting to be discovered.

Bigger may not be Better for ET

Two ideas from the 1960s and 70s seem unlikely today, but they are still seriously entertained at international conferences on astronomical SETI. These are the classification of extraterrestrial civilizations by Nikolai Kardashev and the idea of Dyson Spheres.

Kardashev said that the power of signals and broadcasts which we might receive would depend of the energy resources available to the transmitting civilization for this purpose. Well we are not putting any energy into transmitting specific signals to other worlds. We're only in the listening business. However, given that ETs more advanced than ourselves are prepared to invest massive amounts of energy in the broadcasting business, Kardashev has classified extraterrestrial civilizations according to their available energy resources, a proportion of which may be used for interstellar communications.

Type One civilizations would be at about our level, depending as we do on that tiny proportion of the Sun's total energy output which strikes the Earth, something like 100,000,000,000,000,000 Watts.

Type Two civilizations would be able to use all the energy output of their star (sun). With a star like the Sun this would be about 4 x 100,000,000,000,000,000,000,000,000 Watts. How a Type Two civilization would so capture all of its sun's energy was not clear until Dyson suggested his "Dyson Spheres" (see below).

Type Three civilizations, the energy guzzlers of the cosmos, would be able to exploit the whole energy output of their galaxy, which, if comparable to our Milky Way, would provide about 4 x 10,000,000,000,000,000,000,000,000,000,000,000,000 Watts.

Kardashev was still pursuing this line of thought in 1992 at an international SETI symposium. He speculated that the level of development in a civilization would be expressed in the amount of energy used, and that the most advanced civilizations would build the largest structures. Such structures, he speculated, would radiate in the infrared at between 3 degrees Kelvin (3 degrees above absolute zero) to 300 degrees Kelvin. For structures at a temperature of 300 degrees K. there is a maximum emission of radiation at 15 to 20 micrometres, but none of the few observations so far made in this area show any evidence of ET's enthusiasm for the building industry.

This idea that the more advanced a civilization, the more energy it will use is based on our growing use of energy in the relatively brief period of our technological times. It may be wrong to assume that our demands for more energy will go on forever. Our civilization may use an increasing amount of energy into the foreseeable future, but what about the unforeseeable future in a few thousand years time? The human race may reach a stage where enough energy is available to meet all desirable needs.

Freeman Dyson's "Dyson Spheres", which he suggested in 1959 and again in 1966, so impressed some astronomers that they searched for them. Dyson suggested that super civilizations, in their lust for more energy, might use the material of their planetary systems to build hollow spheres about their suns. In this way they could collect all the energy radiated and not lose almost all of it to outer space, as we do in the Solar System.

Dyson calculated that such a sphere whose shell was only metres thick would be stable for habitation, but subsequent calculations showed that this would not be so. Dyson then produced a revised model in which the shell was composed of vast numbers of space colonies. Space colonies would obviously be a better way to use the Sun's available energy, and, importantly, they could be spread out in orbits throughout the Solar System.

The problem for astronomers willing to try and detect a Dyson Sphere has been that the infrared radiation from its surface would be similar to that coming from newly forming stars. It looks, therefore, as if Dyson's hypothesis is not testable.

My immediate thought on seeing the initial model of a Dyson Sphere was that it might be a little too hot for comfort. With much of the energy being radiated back into what we could call inner space from the inside surface of the sphere, it would soon become rather warm. My second thought concerned the problem of containing an atmosphere on the inside surface of the sphere with an ozone layer to protect life against those lethal parts of the Sun's radiation. But vast numbers of space colonies, having their own individual atmospheres enclosed, would solve these problems.

Spaceship Spotting

Another idea which is less impressive than Dyson Spheres is spaceship spotting. The idea is based on the dubious assumption that extraterrestrials who are thousands of years ahead of us will be using the ultimate in dangerous fuel to propel themselves at speeds approaching that of light. The fuel they would be using is antimatter, and energy from its use would come from the mutual annihilation of our kind of matter and antimatter, when the two come into contact. It is considered the ultimate in energy sources only because it is a hundred percent efficient: all matter in the interaction is transformed into energy. We can imagine how ultimate this could be by comparison with what happens in a hydrogen bomb explosion when less than one percent of matter is released as energy.

In a way it's surprising that so many learned papers on space propulsion have dealt with this most potent means of self-destruction. The assumption that matter-antimatter annihilation would be used in space propulsion looks like chauvinism. It's the best way physicists can think of, based on current knowledge. It allows them to do mathematics on the process and come up with definite numbers to describe what would happen if anyone was reckless enough to travel through space for years with a load of antimatter on board. However, the idea does provide a testable hypothesis, which makes it seem less crazy – we should always be sympathetic to testable hypotheses in science. Calculations show that antimatter-matter annihilation on the scale needed to drive a spaceship would produce an observable' quantity of gamma-ray radiation (see Fig. 6.4). In theory, a spaceship using antimatter and travelling at a significant fraction of the speed of light, would show up as a gamma-ray source moving across the sky at up to a hundred times faster than any natural source of gamma-rays known to astronomers. A spaceship might be tracked by its gamma-rays at distances of 300 to 1,000 light-years. The problem for SETI observers is that gamma-rays don't penetrate the Earth's atmosphere. Any tracking of alien spaceships propelled through space by antimatter will have to be done from satellite observatories.

I find it hard to believe that antimatter-matter annihilation will be involved in future spaceship propulsion just because it is the ultimate

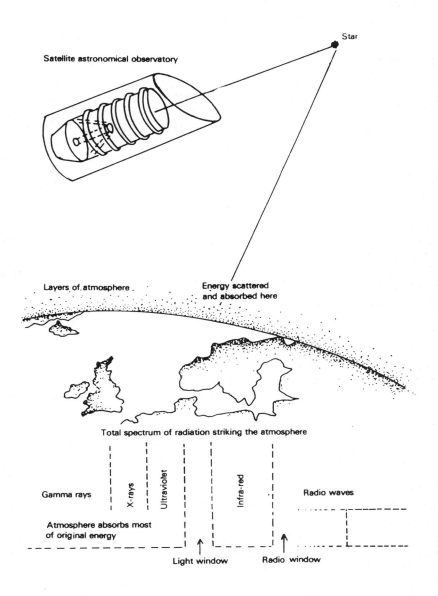

Fig. 6.4: Most radition from the universe never reaches the Earth's surface and the telescopes of ground-based astronomers.

source of energy that we can currently envisage from available science. What seems more likely is that we have not yet discovered the science which will form the basis of the ultimate in space propulsion. Can we expect to have discovered all the physics there is to know in this universe after a few centuries, even though physics is the most advanced of the sciences? A reasonable answer is "No". Therefore, there is more physics to discover, some of which we may be able to apply to produce a revolution in space technology. Anyone interested in our future in space should, therefore, back fundamental physics. The physicists may feel a little uncomfortable about this, but they are our only hope for the "humanization of space", as Gerard O'Neill used to prefer to describe our possible future exploitation of space.

Ghostly Particles

Some scientists in SETI have considered the possibility that ET may broadcast with neutrinos, particles like sub-nuclear ghosts which travel at the speed of light and hardly interact with anything in the universe. On Earth, neutrinos emerge from natural radioactivity, and physicists produce them in nuclear reactors and in their high-energy accelerators with which they probe the nature of physical reality.

In one way neutrinos seem a good candidate since nothing in the Galaxy is likely to stop them. They would travel on when light and radio waves could not. But they are not easy to detect. When Supernova 1987A provided one of the most powerful explosions in the universe, astronomers detected 20 neutrinos over a period of about 12 seconds, but their calculations showed that in that particular explosion, which occurred in the large Magellanic Cloud, about 10 followed by 58 noughts of neutrinos were ejected into space. During the 12 seconds in which 20 neutrinos were detected here, a thousand billion neutrinos passed through every square centimetre of the Earth's surface.

So we have a problem. Our technology is not up to detecting messages coded in neutrinos. Currently, enormous detectors are needed to trap the odd neutrino out of billions passing through. The University of Pennsylvania has a detector deep in a mine which consists of a vessel containing 100,000 gallons of a compound of chlorine. When a neutrino strikes the nucleus of a chlorine atom it forms an atom of argon. Argon is a radioactive gas which can be detected by the apparatus. One jocular physicist has suggested that the currently undetectable nature of neutrinos may be in their favour with really advanced civilizations. The generation and detection of neutrinos is so difficult that only really advanced civilizations will be able to use them to transmit and receive communications, thus avoiding time-wasting conversations with technological infants like us.

Faster than Light

Could it be that 'faster than light' communications (something based on tachyons) are possible? ETs may not be using radio at all, bearing in mind that the last civilization in the Galaxy to reach technological status could be a million years ahead of us. Perhaps, unknown to us, tachyons offer one distinct channel for communications, so leaving behind the need for everyone in the Galaxy to guess what frequencies other worlds may be using.

The concept of tachyons, the theoretical particles that can travel faster than light, is at present, however, little more than speculation, though physicists currently envisage them as the only means by which faster-than-light interstellar communications may be achieved. There is no limit to the speed of tachyons, except that they cannot travel slower than the speed of light. Although theoretical work on tachyons has been convincing enough to persuade a few physicists to set up apparatus and search for them – so far without success – the majority of physicists think that tachyons do not exist. But they cannot be entirely ruled out at present because the current theoretical framework of physics allows them to exist. We have seen before that sub-atomic particles of theory have subsequently been discovered, even when their existence seemed very improbable – like that of the neutrino. However, unlike such sub-atomic particles (the existence of the neutrino was necessary to explain basic aspects of the physical world) the existence of tachyons is not necessary to explain anything. Yet if they do exist, they could completely change the significance of interstellar communications – that is, providing it is possible to build tachyon transmitters and receivers. I think that we can assume that ETs would not be using microwaves or any other section of the electromagnetic spectrum for their interstellar communications if a basis exists in nature for something far more effective.

Benevolent ETs

Even if ETs are rare and have only radio for their communications, there could still be a few super civilizations beaming their messages across the Galaxy, or to other galaxies. Any reply that anyone could send might take thousands or millions of years, so two-way communications could not take place. Societies may, however, wish to transmit information about themselves without expecting a reply, as we have with the spacecraft Pioneer 10 and 11 and Voyager 1 and 2. These will undoubtedly journey through outer space with virtually no chance of being seen again. In contrast, an automatic transmitter in space, repeating an information-loaded message for millions of years, might at least be detected.

It is also feasible that the individual members of some super civilizations live for thousands of years, long enough perhaps to have their messages acknowledged. There seems no obstacle to great longevity that we cannot envisage an advanced society overcoming. They might even be immortal electronic beings, but for a short-lived species like ourselves, the existence of tachyons or their equivalent may be our only hope of an interstellar dialogue.

It can be argued that astronomers everywhere (in whatever ET form and wherever they happen to be in the universe, in both time and space) will always be collecting information about stars and other galaxies. Our present knowledge of the universe depends almost entirely upon one section or other of the electromagnetic spectrum, because all matter in the universe which is not at absolute zero radiates electromagnetic radiation from gamma rays to radio waves. Therefore, the technology that collects information about the universe by receiving electromagnetic radiation is unlikely to be a temporary technology.

Even if a more rapid carrier of information exists for communicating across interstellar distances, some ETs may still send 'call signals' in one section or another of the electromagnetic spectrum because they will know that astronomers somewhere will be receiving on such frequencies. Some ETs may, therefore, choose frequencies of astronomical significance – frequencies that they know astronomers will be studying.

New Physics

In speculating about a new level of communications technology that might solve the problems of detecting ET's broadcasts, we should consider the odd position of research in fundamental physics. This area of science has grown enormously since 1945, with increasingly more powerful particle accelerators being built to enable physicists to study the sub-nuclear world and the forces which govern the fundamental particles of matter. It is the most costly area of scientific research, yet it has discovered little applicable knowledge compared with physics of the past century and the early decades of this one. Nevertheless, this research has to be continued, otherwise we will never understand the nature of matter and the forces which determine its behaviour. We could speculate that the relatively easy discoveries have already been made, even though they haven't always looked easy, and that the discoveries in physics in the future, which may provide knowledge to transform the world, will be far more difficult to come by.

Fundamental physics (particle physics) is the most difficult area of scientific research, but the future discoveries which might provide the knowledge base for a new means of communications and a new level in space propulsion can only come from this field. Of course, one cannot say that it will. We can only say that no other area of science can provide it.

There is another way of looking at this subject. The scientists investigating matter at a sub-nuclear level and the forces operating within the atomic nucleus have provided us with new understanding about the basic fabric of the universe. Our understanding and appreciation of the universe has been greatly enhanced, but the components of the nucleus, the elusive quarks, which form the protons and neutrons and other particles, are still phantoms of an accepted theory. No one has detected them, and, according to the particle physicists, it seems that they may remain undetectable. Fundamental physics today looks as complicated as anything could be, highly theoretical and very uncertain. The big breakthroughs to new science which can provide technological applications may be achieved in the future, but, on the other hand, they may not. Here we come to "ceilings". Have the major discoveries in physics which can be applied already been made? Is that *it*, as far as the universe is concerned? Will technological advances from now on have to be based on the physics already known? Is it that physics, the most advanced of the sciences, is already near a relatively low ceiling to complete understanding of the physical universe? The history of science indicates that this is not so. And whether it is or not we cannot know. One cannot predict future science. There is, therefore, no alternative but to press on with research.

Better Receivers

For the present, given that electromagnetic radiation is the only possible carrier of interstellar communications, the radio technology used in current SETI projects is a long way from any conceivable plateau of perfectability. The technology is improving so rapidly that improvements will undoubtedly continue to be made in the decades ahead. Since astronomers are putting telescopes of various kinds into space, and may eventually have special telescopes there for SETI, we should perhaps ask when the 'limit of technical perfectibility' may be reached in this technology. The question is necessary because we can surely expect that ET signals would be transmitted for a level of reception already at the plateau of technical perfectibility in electromagnetic communications. This plateau would probably include having receivers in space and not under an atmosphere. Whatever section of the electromagnetic spectrum is used for interstellar communications – if it is used – it may not necessarily penetrate a planetary atmosphere. Since we have been able to venture into space barely 200 years after the start of the Industrial Revolution, we can expect that virtually all ETs will be in space with space stations and space colonies, and so on. Another few hundred years and the Solar System may be thoroughly explored, with the number of space colonies increasing at an exponential rate. By that stage, there would be many advanced astronomical facilities in space capable of receiving ET transmissions. Knowing this as a probable development for technological species, transmitting civilizations may disregard the blanketing effect of a planetary atmosphere on sections of the electromagnetic spectrum.

I remember a well-known physicist discussing the problem of the atmosphere some 30 years ago and maintaining that advanced ETs would make an allowance for receivers being restricted to planetary surfaces. This just shows how quickly our ideas change with our technological progress. ET signals may well penetrate our atmosphere, but we cannot expect them to have been selected for that reason. Although microwaves between the frequencies of 1 to 10 GHz do penetrate our atmosphere, this band is favoured in searches because it includes the universal hydrogen and hydroxyl lines and would make effective use of an ETs available energy.

Interstellar Eavesdropping

Of course, we have to allow for the great antiquity of any communications network which may exist within the Galaxy. Apart from call signals and messages transmitted by ETs who are isolated, the main transmissions are not likely to be for us – having been in the electromagnetic communications business for less than a century. So what about the possibility of our doing some eavesdropping?

Our own radio and television broadcasts have already travelled 75 light-years into space. Powerful defence radar systems are also contributing to this expanding sphere of radiation. Such leakage from communications and radar systems may be less detectable than a signal specifically transmitted for detection, but it shows that eavesdropping on the communications of other worlds may be possible.

Woodruff Sullivan and Stephen Knowles have investigated the possibility of such eavesdropping. At a SETI symposium in 1984 at Boston University, they described their research. They initially decided to discover what any interested ET might be able to detect if it eavesdropped in our direction. They observed our television broadcasts reflected from the Moon, using the largest radio telescope in the world, the 1,000-metre dish at Arecibo. The reflective Moon provided the equivalent of a radio picture of Earth from deep space. One surprise was that the most powerful reflected signal turned out to be the US Navy's space surveillance radar, of which Sullivan and Knowles were completely unaware. "The Moon, like the Earth, is remarkably bright in radio wavelengths," they said. "It is a mirror of our technical civilization."

It could be that our television and radar will be the cause of the first ET signal being transmitted in our direction. There are about 100 stars close enough for our broadcasts to have been detected already. Thus, as our sphere of radiation from communications and radar expands into space, the probability increases that we might just receive a strong and unmistakable ET signal in reply. In my view our period of broadcasting has been far too short to be significant, when compared with the spectral lines of ozone and oxygen which the atmosphere has been transmitting into space for more than 350 million years.

The leakage of television broadcasts into space may be only temporary. Within a few decades our transmitting systems could be more efficient and overcome this loss. If peace breaks out, our powerful defence radar would become redundant. Sullivan and Knowles point out, however, that other technological projects which leak radiation into space will follow television and radar. Large solar satellites, for example, may one day provide most of our energy requirements directly from the Sun, transmitting the Sun's energy to Earth in powerful beams of microwaves and leaking radiation into space in the process. Knowles has said that the minimum leakage of radiation to be expected from such a technology might be detectable 100 times further away than our present television and radar.

Another source of future radiation leakage might be powerful beacons for navigation within the Solar System. We can expect the Solar System to become a rather crowded place in the future, with a large amount of routine transport requiring navigational assistance, if ever we discover a practical means of propulsion.

Signalling by Lasers

Soon after lasers were developed, it was suggested that the ultra-narrow beams of pure light (single frequency light) which lasers produce might be a way of communicating across interstellar distances. The first search for extraterrestrial lasers was made from the Copernicus Satellite in 1974, when three nearby stars were scanned for ultraviolet laser lines. In the same year Dr. Shvartsman and colleagues in the then Soviet Union began to use the 6-metre optical telescope at Zelenchuskaya, the world's largest optical telescope, to search for laser signals.

The idea that ETs may have been trying to contact us with laser signals has been criticised by some people who point out that laser beams, unlike radio beams, are visible. We might, therefore, have expected our ancestors in historical times (who were a good deal more aware of the night sky than we are) to have noticed beams of light in the sky. There are no records of any such observations, but then there wouldn't be. ET's laser transmissions would not reach the Earth like a display in a discotheque. The beams would spread and could only be detected with the aid of an optical telescope.

Interest in the possible detection of laser signals has greatly increased in recent years, and Optical SETI, as it is called, is now holding its own scientific conferences. Those involved believe that main-stream astronomical SETI may be concentrating too much on microwaves. They point out that light can carry vastly more data because the wavelengths of light are about a million times shorter than microwaves, and that any ETs using highly focused lasers for interstellar communications could make a big saving on their energy bills. With tightly focused laser beams, the ETs could concentrate all their available energy on their targets. And they could put all this energy into a frequency that would stand out against the light from their sun. It would be a frequency of a substance that could not possibly be radiating from a star (sun).

The scenario is that they would focus on neighbouring planetary systems which their astronomers had already studied, as we are just beginning to do. Knowing your target planetary system would be essential for laser-beam transmissions. The big problem is that everything in space is on the move, so that a laser transmitter in one planetary system would have to move its beam in perfect co-ordination with the target planetary system. Keep in mind that the photons of the laser beam would be travelling at the speed of light. They would therefore not reach their target for some years, depending on how many light-years had to be crossed. Meanwhile, as the photons were on their way, the target planetary system would have been moving through space at a velocity of hundreds of kilometres a second. Now to transmit a laser beam at a target which is several light-years away and moving at that speed – and to keep your laser beam on that target while you unload your message – is not going to be easy. ETs in this line of interstellar communications will have had to master advanced targeting technology – something which we won't be able to do in the immediate future.

What, then must we do to detect ET's laser messages? The first step is to detect an emission line in the spectrum of a neighbouring star like the Sun. In theory, ET's laser beam will provide a frequency (and, therefore, a spectral line) which could not possibly come from the radiation of a sun-like star. An enormous amount of energy would have to be concentrated into that frequency for us to see it against the background radiation, but, in theory, it could be done with a very tightly focused beam.

Now, detecting that significant spectral line is the easy part, if there is an easy part in this exercise. It would be a great discovery, but that spectral line could only tell us that we have found a signal which someone out there has transmitted. We wouldn't obtain any more information from it. The next step would be to tune into the frequency of the artificial spectral line with the latest in laser technology. We would have to assume that information would come in the form of brief pulses of the laser frequency, like fantastically short morse code signals. Anyway, that, in theory, is how it would be done.

Those who believe in optical SETI do have a current advantage. There has been an enormous amount of costly research and development in laser technology in recent years. The Star Wars program moved the subject along rather quickly, but apart from its military applications, the use of lasers in communications technology is of growing commercial interest. Dr. Stuart Kingsley, of Fiberdyne Optoelectronics in Ohio, is one of the leading figures in Optical SETI. His belief in the ability of ETs to master the targeting problems involved has motivated him to build an optical SETI observatory at his home. He and his colleagues have also encouraged others to set up their own SETI observatories. They say that telescopes with 6 inch optics, and larger, would enable observers to search the nearest sun-like stars – presumably for that hypothetical spectral line. Stuart Kingsley opened his optical SETI observatory in 1993 and organised a large conference on optical SETI in Los Angeles in the same year. Anyone interested in becoming an optical SETI observer could do no better than contact Dr. Kingsley. (See Appendix 1).

Signs of Alien Technology

It might be possible to detect nuclear fusion technology in space. An original search in 1983 by Drs. Franciso Valdes and Robert Freitas at the Hat Creek Radio Observatory in California attempted to do so. They were looking for the line of radioactive tritium (H_3, an isotope of hydrogen), a by-product of nuclear fusion technology. Atoms of tritium radiate microwaves at 1516 MHz to produce this line, which is conveniently placed within the microwave band and could be easily observed.

If advanced ETs are involved in the nuclear fusion business, so the theory goes, perhaps carrying out the task of energy generation in space, then there may be enough of this by-product in the vicinity of their star (sun) to be detectable. The detection of a strong signal on this line would be very significant because there exists no known natural source of tritium in space and it has a half-life of only 12.6 years. Its production would, therefore, have to be continuous for it to exist at all.

Motives: Theirs and Ours

Our assumptions of the social and technological superiority of ETs leads us to anticipate that *their* motives for signalling to new civilizations and our motives for searching for their signal may be different. They will already know the score. We want to escape from our ignorance and isolation. Contacting new civilizations may be routine for them. There is nothing routine about our search. We want to know whether or not life and intelligence exist beyond the Earth, and our search for an intelligent signal is a means of finding out. Later, we will certainly explore the Moon and the rest of the Solar System where ET visiting cards could possibly have been left during the past four billion years – and more probably during the past 350 million years. But for the present, as far as science is concerned, the answer to our most fundamental question may be in an ET signal which the astronomers in SETI may or may not find. For all we know, life on Earth may be a freak event in the universe. We may be an aberration of matter, rather than, as we prefer to think, an inevitable product of the innate processes of nature and an essential element in the history of the universe, from its 'big bang' birth to we know not what. The evolution of complexity of matter from the simplest atom to the human brain can be only a small part of that history. To discover something of our place in it is the driving motive behind SETI.

Some critics point out our unsuitability for a correspondence that may take thousands of years. As our life span is usually some way short of 100 years, the criticism has some justification. Nevertheless, just the detection of an intelligent signal would justify all SETI projects. Those two persistent questions, "Is there life beyond the Earth?" and "Are there intelligent beings elsewhere in the universe?" would both, at last, be answered. "At one fell swoop," as Shakespeare said. Later, a flow of information might start a new adventure for our civilization, although nothing could equal in significance the first detection of that signal. It would be the most important discovery in history. For us the distance of the source would not greatly matter, except that its distance from us might indicate the abundance, or otherwise, of transmitting ETs.

We would not expect to open a dialogue in the foreseeable future, and maybe it would never be possible. Perhaps only a few old and stable civilizations contribute to the Immortal Network. They might be more able and ready to establish permanent transmitters in space, and the rarer the evolution of technological intelligence is, the more interested they may be in signalling their presence. For this reason, the argument against their being any ET signals to detect, if the abundance of ETs falls below a certain number, is really invalid. The motive for signalling will not evaporate if the evolution of ETs is known to be very rare, providing that some ETs survive to become very advanced.

That Mysterious Signal

The type of signal that might come from ET has, in fact, already been discovered. One evening late in 1967, at the Royal Institution in London, Nobel laureate Melvin Calvin shocked us somewhat when he disclosed in a lecture on the origin of life that a radio source pulsating with incredible precision had just been discovered by radio astronomers at Cambridge. The signal, he said, was the kind we might expect to receive from intelligent life in other planetary systems. He said no more, but several days later we learned that a new astronomical phenomenon, a pulsar, had been discovered.

The Cambridge astronomers themselves at first wondered if they had discovered an intelligent signal. Three weeks passed before they decided that they had not. It was not long before similar objects, widely separated in the Galaxy, were being detected by other radio astronomers in other countries, as well as at Cambridge and Jodrell Bank. Each new issue of the journal "Nature" reported a new pulsar, or so it seemed at the time. We were surrounded by pulsars, and a phenomenon repeated again and again had to be a natural one. Astronomers had, in fact, discovered the radiation from rapidly spinning neutron stars.

Now let us look at the claims that extraterrestrial intelligence has already arrived here on Earth: from ancient historical times, when they were perceived to come in chariots of fire, to today's reports of flying saucers. We must examine these claims against a background of relevant scientific information because if just one of those many accounts of extraterrestrial visitors happens to be true, we would have to come to a profound and rather discomforting conclusion, which we will consider in the next chapter. It would be that our galaxy does, indeed, contain other technological beings and that they are right here on our celestial doorstep.

Chapter Seven

Ancient Astronauts ... and all that

Many accounts of visiting extraterrestrial s have been published in recent years. Their authors take their subjects seriously. They believe in what they write, but they seem oblivious to one item of information that drastically affects the probability of such visits. It is the time problem. Those who search for evidence of ETs in the records of written history can cover, at most, only a few thousand years, whereas any consideration of visits by astronauts from other worlds must cover the past few billion years. It is for that length of time because of the age of the oldest sun-like stars in the Galaxy that ET space technology has been a possibility. On statistical grounds Erich von Daniken's ancient astronauts, to take the best-known writer on historical astronauts, are not ancient enough – not by any means!

As the Galaxy is more than ten billion years old, our level of civilization could have been reached a few billion years ago in planetary systems that formed a few billion years before the Solar System. This was possible as soon as stars like the Sun began to form. Therefore, the first technological beings to evolve have had so much time to develop their technologies that we can barely begin to imagine their achievements. In their early days – say a thousand years beyond where we are today – we can imagine their spacecraft journeying from planetary system to planetary system, perhaps even before the Earth existed. Their craft might be crewed by highly intelligent robots and driven across the light-years by the ultimate system of space propulsion, which we may ourselves develop when we know enough physics.

The age of the oldest sun-like stars in the Galaxy is, therefore, very relevant when we are considering the possibility of ET visits. The first civilizations to master the ultimate technology for interstellar travel might have spread throughout the Galaxy. There has been enough time for this, as numerous scientists have pointed out while also pointing out that we don't see any evidence of such a development. But, as a newly emerging technological civilization, we shouldn't expect to. Dozens of small moons of fifty to more than a hundred kilometers across, orbiting the outer planets, have been discovered by NASA spacecraft in recent years, and it is estimated that hundreds more moons remain to be discovered. Consequently, evidence of visitors could be out there in numerous places within the Solar System, and we would know nothing about it. Within a few billion years of technological activity, some of the ETs to have evolved could have stations, colonies or exploratory probes in most planetary systems in the Galaxy. Even late arrivals at the technological stage, civilizations developing interstellar travel a few million years ago, have had sufficient time for this. While we have no acceptable evidence that something like this has taken place, certain aspects of the UFO phenomena are sufficiently in line with what we know of the relevant science to justify proper scientific attention*.

As O'Neill has shown, a planetary surface is not the best place for technological development that goes much beyond our present level. The stress upon the home planet would be too great. It, therefore, seems probable that technological civilizations are forced to colonize their planetary systems as a result of population pressures and shortages of energy and resources. With the advanced space technology that they develop, they might conceivably go on to enter the planetary systems of other stars, building space habitats for themselves by mining bodies like the asteroids.

We can see how our own development could make the building of space colonies a very desirable activity. In space all the energy anyone would need would be free – obtained directly from the Sun. But until we know enough physics to take a quantum leap in the space propulsion business we are not going very far in the space age. No nation these days is going to fund the first space colony: the transport costs with current rocket systems would be too great. Gerard O'Neill's dream can only become a reality when trips to the Moon become as practical as flying the Atlantic. This can only happen if the physicists gain the knowledge needed to develop a new level in space propul-

---

* See "The UFO Phenomena".

sion. If this knowledge does not exist for the development of space technology, then everyone is going to remain at home, including all those ET visitors who could otherwise have visited the Solar System any time during the past few billion years.

Now, whereas we cannot easily imagine beings of super intelligence leaving the facilities of their advanced civilizations to journey for decades through the cold emptiness of interstellar space, we can imagine such journeys with artificial intelligence (robots) in control. If biological beings were needed, the robots might build a suitable space colony for them before synthesizing the genes of the race on the home planet, so starting a first generation of colonists, though a robot as mother-substitute might create a few biological and psychological problems.

Given the progress of biology and computer science, such a scenario might be possible for us within a few centuries. Would we want to carry out such colonization? Our species has been biologically driven to spread our genes and to take over as much territory as possible. Perhaps more advanced societies would not see the sense of extending such urges to the colonization of other planetary systems. New information might be more important to them than establishing new territories. There are also the biological dangers of an alien biosphere to consider. Biological ETs would not be compatible with the biosphere of Earth. They wouldn't be able to use our food because the basic molecular biology would be different. Neither would they have any biological protection against our abundant microbes. This is the message from fundamental biology.

The Long History of ETs in the Galaxy

The age of the Galaxy is fundamental to our thinking about the human situation in relation to possible life beyond the Earth. If the Galaxy were significantly younger, not much older than the Sun, then we could entertain the thought that we are among the first wave of technological species to have evolved; and there would be no apparent paradox in the absence of evidence of ET visits. In a Galaxy more than twice the age of the Sun, however, we cannot be amongst the first if life is part of the great scheme of things.

One does hear a great deal about this paradox, as posed by Fermi's question many years ago, but it is only an apparent paradox. As the old saying goes, "absence of evidence is not the same as evidence of absence." We could speculate that large ET space colonies are within the Solar System and the source of the UFO phenomena. No one could state definitely that this is not so when 99 per cent of the Solar System remains unknown to us at the level needed to detect such colonies. It was only in 1979 that two new moons of Jupiter were discovered. The first, photographed by Voyager 1, is 70-80 kilometres across; the second, photographed by Voyager 2, is 30-40 kilometres across. Since then Voyager 2 has discovered ten previously unknown moons orbiting Uranus. Most are about 70 kilometres in diameter, with one 170 kilometres across! Since their discovery, NASA has announced reasons for thinking that many more such moons orbit Uranus.

History of the Galaxy

Let us briefly consider the age and history of the Galaxy. We need to know how long stars like the Sun, with its range and abundance of heavy elements, have been forming. Heavy elements (mainly metals) have been essential for the growth of our civilization, and the same would apply on other worlds. The incorporation of heavy elements into earlier planetary systems obviously depended on these elements having been synthesised in the early history of the Galaxy, probably by generations of very massive and short-lived stars. The more massive a star, the shorter its life span.

All elements heavier than hydrogen and helium (the two lightest) have been synthesised within stars. Helium is thought to have existed since the 'big bang', but it is also continuously formed by the stars. The main energy source in all stable stars comes from the 'burning' of hydrogen into helium (the nuclear fusion of the hydrogen bomb). Only stars provide enough heat to form elements heavier than helium. All elements heavier than iron (which at an atomic weight of 56 is 'halfway up' the atomic scale) can be formed only by stars several times more massive than the Sun when they end their life cycles in supernovae explosions.

Many astronomers think that the first massive stars carried out such synthesis relatively quickly. One reason for thinking so is that the spectral lines of heavy elements exist in the spectra of all stars. These lines (see Fig. 4.3) are the finger-prints of the stars. They show what the stars are made of. Each element has its own distinct set of lines because each element absorbs radiation and radiates at its own specific wavelengths, thus producing lines which can be observed. Most astronomers, therefore, think that the elements which can be so observed have existed in their present relative abundance for the greater part of the Galaxy's history. The Galaxy would have looked more or less as it does today after its initial few hundred million years of evolution.

Astronomers have found no stars without a proportion of heavy elements, although some have far less than the Sun. A star listed astronomically as HD 122563 has the smallest known proportion of heavy elements – reported to be 300 times less than in the Sun. But stars like HD 122563 are very rare and among the oldest in the Galaxy. Older stars, the first stars, no longer shine. Almost all must have consumed their nuclear fuel long ago, although they will still exist as celestial cinders or as black holes.

The first stars could not have been like the stars that formed at a later stage. Only the original elements of the universe, hydrogen and helium, were available at their formation. They must have initially lacked completely all heavier elements. Such stars are the 'missing links' of stellar evolution, and any that still shine must be very small stars indeed. Being of small mass they would 'burn' slowly and have a long life cycle.

The important point for our subject is that most stars, many of which are older than the Sun, have an abundance of heavy elements. This suggests that any planets which they may possess will not differ much in composition from those of the Solar System. Obviously, rocky planets like Mercury, Mars, Venus and Earth could not form unless the protostar which gave them birth had sufficient heavy elements.

Age of the Galaxy

Astronomers use four independent methods to calculate the age of the Galaxy. As each method gives a roughly similar age, one can safely conclude that the Galaxy is at least ten billion years old. The methods are:

¤ The radioactive dating of the Galaxy which depends on the present ratios of uranium 235 to uranium 238, thorium 232 to uranium 238, lead 244 to uranium 238, and rhenium to osmium. The ratios that exist today depend on when these elements were formed by massive stars in the Galaxy. Since we know the atomic decay rates for each element, we can work out (from the present ratios) when these elements were first formed in the Galaxy. We thus have four independent radioactive clocks which give an age for the Galaxy of between 10 to 20 billion years.

¤   If we accept (as most astronomers do) that the universe has been expanding since the 'big bang', then the red-shifts in the spectra of galaxies and other extragalactic objects indicate the rate of expansion of the universe, and so provide a measure of its age. By going back in time, we can reach a point before which the density of matter was too great to have allowed galaxies to form.

¤   The universal background radiation of three degrees Kelvin (that is, three degrees above absolute zero), which Pensias and Wilson discovered in 1963, and for which discovery they received a Nobel Prize in 1978, is generally accepted as the energy from the initial fireball. With the expansion of the universe this has dissipated from many millions of degrees to 3 degrees Kelvin. We have here, therefore, additional support for the age of the universe (and the age of galaxies) from its expansion since the 'big bang'. The age of the universe thus calculated is around 15 billion years.

¤   The Galaxy must be older than its oldest stars, and the ages of its oldest stars can be estimated. The oldest collections of stars exist in what are called globular clusters, of which there are over 100, situated mainly in the halo of the Galaxy. Each globular cluster consists of hundreds of thousands of stars. All the stars in each globular cluster must have formed at the same time in the same conditions and from the same cloud of matter, so that initially all stars in each cluster had roughly the same composition. There was just one variable: their original masses were different, and this accounts for their present observable differences. As gravity has permanently locked together the stars of each globular cluster, astronomers can compare the results of billions of years of stellar evolution – because the rate at which stars within a cluster have evolved to their present observable state has been determined solely by their original mass. Differences in mass have important consequences for stars. The greater the mass, the faster the rate at which a star 'burns' its substance. Indeed, the luminosity of a star, which results from its rate of 'burning' hydrogen into helium, increases dramatically with increased mass. For example, a star ten times the mass of the Sun will 'burn up' its substance 1,000 times faster. Massive stars thus pass rapidly through the stages of stellar evolution to end as supernovae, neutron stars or black holes, depending upon their original mass. Very massive stars, perhaps 20 to 30 times the Sun's mass, can remain stable only for a few million years. Yet stars of low mass have long lifetimes. A star just 10 per cent less massive than the Sun should remain stable for about 15 billion years. A star 25 per cent less massive will last even longer, with a life expectancy twice that of the Sun. So stars of about the mass of the Sun and less will have life spans of ten billion years and more. The Sun in its senility, in about five billion years time, will become a white dwarf. It will then have reached the end of its active life cycle. Many white dwarfs which were once like the Sun exist in globular clusters.

However, a sun-like star may be physically stable and yet no longer permit life on a habitable planet. Astrophysicists have calculated that in less than a billion years the Sun will be making the Earth too hot for life. But a lot can happen in a billion years. Half a billion years ago, the most advanced life-forms on Earth were the primitive ancestors of the first fishes.

Visits to Earth

These four separate lines of enquiry lead us to think that the Galaxy has been in a condition similar to its present one for about ten billion years, so that, in theory, ETs or their exploratory probes could have visited the Earth at any time since its formation. A little arithmetic will show the implication of this, and why claims that we have been visited in historical times, or are being visited today, would have to be backed up with indisputable scientific evidence.

To make the arithmetic easy, we will let the Earth settle for a few hundred million years after its formation before we entertain visitors. Let us say that they could have arrived at any time during the past four billion years, instead of 4.6 billion years, the accepted age of the Earth which has been determined by various methods, including analyses of meteorites and Moon rocks. Let us also assume, to make the arithmetic easy, that the probability of visits remains constant during the four billion year period. (Actually, we could expect the probability of visits to increase with time, but we'll come to that later.)

Most of the ancient astronauts popularised in newspapers and books are supposed to have visited within the past 4,000 years of human history. The probability of just one visit in this period rather than at any other time in Earth history is, therefore, 4,000 years into 4,000,000,000 years. This is the same as 1,000 into 1,000,000,000 or

1 into 1,000,000. Does this mean that to make just one visit statistically probable in historical times (in the past 4,000 years) requires that there were a million ET visits to the Earth since its formation? No, it's more complicated than that. We must allow that the probability of a visit to Earth increases as the Galaxy gets older and more technological species evolve. For ETs to have visited the Earth in historical times, or in recent years as the occupants of flying saucers, our Galaxy would have to be teaming with interstellar travellers. ETs would have to be established in a vast number of planetary systems, including our own, constantly studying and monitoring developments. Otherwise, visits from those historical astronauts and occupants of flying saucers would be too great a coincidence to be credible.

ETIs who travel from their home planets to visit us, as science fiction writers have described again and again, are not probable. We should not expect such visitors unless they can slip through one of those "worm holes" so popular with theoretical physicists, and arrive here in a few days. Our difficulty in trying to assess the situation is that we really don't know what may be possible. For societies with more advanced science and technologies, crossing the light-years may not be as difficult as it seems to us.

If interstellar travel has been a routine activity for a few billion years, our presence may be well-documented, especially if 'blue planets' like the Earth are very rare. It has been suggested that for us to have been left undisturbed for so long we must be in a sort of planetary nature reserve. Presumably in such a situation there would be no motive for ETs to leave visiting cards on Earth, or on the Moon. You don't leave signs in a National Park for the chimps to see that you've visited them. However, we could also speculate that our planetary system has been left undisturbed because if we go into space, as part of our future development as an advanced civilization, we will need the material resources of the Moon and the asteroids. In a Galaxy full of ETs this need might be recognised and the resources of planetary systems with flourishing biospheres left intact.

Alternative Scenario

Let us now assume that the planetary systems of our Galaxy have not been explored during the past few billion years, and that our presence is not recorded by all advanced civilizations on the Immortal Network. In short, that we are not in a planetary zoo surrounded by ET activity of which we are unaware, and that any visits during Earth history would be few and widely separated in time. In this case 'visiting cards' are worth consideration, since they could have been left at any time during the past few billion years .

It is hard to imagine a species like ourselves, with the motivation to develop high technology and to explore the universe, who would not leave a sign of its visit after crossing interstellar space, especially if that crossing was very difficult. They might want to do no more than we have done many times on Earth: simply to mark the spot. It does seem improbable that they would act as Daniken and other writers have claimed, by putting their imprint on some ephemeral relic, like The Pyramids, that would last at best a few thousand years.

Let's imagine that they (or their intelligent spacecraft or robots, if they do not make long journeys themselves) came to the Solar System sometime in the past few billion years. That is, since life has been evolving and erosion has been a major force in shaping the Earth. What kind of site would they choose?

There is no reason to suppose that ETs would expect a reply to their messages deposited on, or near to, any world that they, or their robots, may have visited. Radio astronomers in the United States have sent messages to distant stars with no expectation of contacting anyone. Their action was simply a tribute to the idea that intelligence lies 'out there'. The pictures and recordings in and on the Pioneer and Voyager spacecraft are similarly motivated. The purpose of the Pioneer and Voyager probes has been the exploration of the outer planets, and they and their messages will almost certainly never be seen again as they journey through interstellar space, even though they should remain intact for many millions of years. Should we, therefore, credit ETs with less generosity of spirit in their gestures towards propagating the fruits of their intelligence? Furthermore, if, when visiting the Earth long ago, they foresaw the possible evolution of a technological species, they may have found some secure yet distinctive site at which to leave a message.

Evidence on the Moon?

Where could a site be secure for millions of years? Not on Earth. Only on a body free from erosion, one like the Moon, could a sign last that long. David R. Scott, Commander of Apollo 15, said that he had great difficulty in coming to terms with the fact that a large rock in front of him on the Moon had been there, virtually unchanged, for more than 500 million years – before there was any land life on Earth. Alien astronauts landing on the Moon a billion years before Scott would have witnessed much the same scene, and it would not have escaped their notice that this was a good place to leave tokens of their visit to the Solar System. Anything placed on the Moon, from a simple sign to an elaborate data bank, could have been left with the high probability that it would remain intact for a billion years or more. The Moon, one of the most inert worlds in the Solar System, is certainly a likely place for messages from ancient astronauts, if any have ever come our way.

There will be no signs of ancient (historical) astronauts on Earth: unless advanced ETs surround us; unless they occupy the planetary systems of nearby stars; or unless they are established in the outer regions of the Solar System. The idea that ETs would have helped the ancient Egyptians build the great pyramids – or the less ancient South Americans build their pyramids – as signs of visits to Earth is not realistic. Such signs would be too ephemeral and subject to the interference of beings who would not understand the significance of an ET message. Leave the message on the Moon, away from such interference and, more importantly, away from erosion, and there is the possibility of those ancient astronauts being understood by beings sufficiently advanced to cross space from one world to another.

Biological Evidence

There are possible biological consequences of visits in the past, though they could be quickly lost in our biosphere. If biological beings have ever visited the Earth, they would have brought with them their alien microbes. Only sterile electronic astronauts would not carry an alien biology into the planets they visited.

Two Japanese scientists, whose research is described in Chapter 9, have ignored the probable problems for alien life in our biosphere and have suggested that ETs may have tried to communicate with us biologically. They have even suggested that the evidence may still be around to discover. This seems rather fanciful. It seems more likely that any alien organisms (micro-organisms) arriving with ancient astronauts would either quickly die out or increase at the expense of Earthly forms, depending on their liking for conditions here. Admittedly, a large proportion of the Earth's living matter by weight is made up of micro-organisms, so there could be something hidden in the micro-world, although it seems unlikely.

So what can we make of "ancient astronaut" stories? We would need something like exponential growth of colonization in the Galaxy to make ET visits to the Solar System plausible in historical times. Alternatively, there has to be an easy means of crossing the light-years by worm holes or by distorting space-time, or some other means beyond current imagination. Otherwise, visits during human history rather than during some other period of the past few billion years would seem improbable. However, given that interstellar travel is easy and that the ETs have a monitoring base in most planetary systems with an earth-like planet, then, at a time when our civilization is developing so rapidly, we might expect to witness activity by our counterparts from other worlds, or by the robotic servants. It would not, perhaps, be the actual ETs themselves who would be engaging in this activity – if they are biological entities. An alien biosphere such as the Earth, as we have already seen, would be the last place for a visiting ET to spend his holidays. There would be no biologically compatible food – but plenty of potential danger from micro-organisms.

Let's now look at the ways by which the ETs of the Galaxy may have crossed interstellar space to reach the Solar System. Strange to say, a couple of the most convincing ideas for interstellar travel have not come from the space technologists, but from a few scientists who have tried to explain the physics behind the most credible UFO reports, in which nuts-and-bolts spacecraft have been described. We have been this way before in science. A few puzzled people, working just beyond the frontiers of what is considered legitimate subject matter for science, may turn out, in the end, to be justified.

Chapter Eight

Could ETs Reach the Solar System?

There are two reasons why we need to consider how it might be possible to travel to the stars. Firstly, to see if we may be able to do so one day (most people in astronautics think we will). Secondly, to see how probable it is that other civilizations may have visited the Solar System. Numerous space technologists and physicists have written technical papers on interstellar space flight. Hundreds have been published in learned journals. Most grant the feasibility of flying to the stars, although only in periods of time exceeding the present human life span. To reach the nearest star in a shorter time, with a crew on board, would take an unattainable amount of energy, even if the most efficient source of energy which physicists can currently theorise about were to be used.

Within fifty years, judging by new ideas for space technology, small automatic probes may travel to the nearest stars at a substantial fraction of the speed of light, reaching their targets in a decade or two. But astronauts will not follow them in spacecraft, as they did to the Moon, because the nearest star is too far away. The late Allen Hynek, who was an astronomy professor at Northwestern University in Illinois, once gave a vivid analogy of the scale involved. He said, "Let the thickness of a playing card represent the distance from the Earth to the Moon. On that scale the nearest star is 19 miles away." This puts the whole business of interstellar travel into perspective and we may have to travel deeper into neighbouring space than the nearest star before we could discover a planetary system with a planet like the Earth.

The Ways to the Stars

To travel faster than light, just as the crews in "Star Trek", we would have to overcome barriers which the laws of the universe appear to have placed in the way. In theory – but based on science that we partially understand – there seem to be only four ways to the stars. They are:

¤ By spacecraft or space probes which travel almost at the speed of light.

¤ By slower craft in which the travellers would survive in suspended animation of some kind (deep-frozen or in hibernation) for most of the voyage.

¤ By travelling in space colonies, self-contained worlds, at relatively slow speeds. In this way, only future generations would eventually explore and colonize other planetary systems. (This seems too uncertain a future for beings capable of the technology.)

¤ By using computers and robots to do the travelling and exploring for us. These advanced artificial intelligences could switch themselves off during the routine periods of a mission. If we add advanced biological techniques to this arrangement, the robots might be able to synthesise the genes of their makers on arrival at a suitable destination. Possibly just the cells of the colonizing species could be carried in suspended animation to other stars, which would be decidedly more practical than carrying large bodies. Once the robots had built a suitable habitat in the new star system, the synthesised genes, or the genetic materials of living cells, could be used to grow the first generation of a new civilization. In this way, an advanced species might colonize other worlds without any individual of that species ever having to leave home.

Speed of Light Flight

Current conventional science states that nothing can travel faster than the speed of light. Einstein's Special Theory of Relativity, published in 1905 and confirmed over many years by a range of observations and experiments, forbids anything being accelerated past the speed of light. As matter is accelerated, its mass increases. Normally, this is undetectable, but the increase in mass rises sharply near the speed of light. This has been confirmed in particle physics where electrons and protons are accelerated in particle accelerators to within 99.9 per cent the speed of light. Accelerators have electro-magnets which send narrow beams of electrons or protons around their rings, some of which have a circumference of several miles. The beams, no thicker than the lead in a pencil, can be accelerated so near to the speed of light that the mass of the particles increases by about 300 times. The amount of energy needed to accelerate anything (a spaceship or a nuclear particle) rises so sharply near the speed of light that any future spacecraft would have to keep their speed some way below that of light. Even at 87 per cent the speed of light, mass is doubled.

Physicists cannot, therefore, accelerate nuclear particles right up the speed of light, though they get to within a fraction of the last one per cent of that speed. According to Einstein, a particle or a spaceship would have infinite mass at the speed of light and, therefore, infinite energy would be needed to accelerate it further. Another potential hazard for "near speed of light" travellers is that particles of dust in the interstellar medium would strike the spacecraft like cannon balls. Even the rarefied hydrogen atoms in space could have a devastating effect as the spacecraft plunged through them.

Energy we may Never Need

The problem of looking at the ways by which we may reach the stars is that we have to base our speculations on our current understanding of physics, which is obviously incomplete. Hundreds of papers have been written by top-class scientists and technologists on interstellar space flight, all attempting to find a practical way of reaching the nearest stars with what science we currently understand. It looks somewhat like the early attempts to fly with the materials and understanding available to inventors at the end of the 19th century. Flying around the world would have seemed an impossible dream.

The reason we cannot see a practical way of flying to the stars may be because we have not yet discovered the science which would make it possible. I say "may be" because that science, that understanding of nature, may not exist, though for our present purposes we must assume that it does. We can see where it should exist if it does exist. It can be discovered only in advanced physics, in the probing of matter and the forces of nature; research which is carried out by particle physicists, experimentalists and theoreticians, using particle accelerators. It therefore seems an uninformed strategy for governments to be cutting back on this research. The Americans have abandoned, for reasons of economy, what would have been the most powerful accelerator on Earth, which they were building in Texas. The only facility now capable of the most advanced experiments in physics is at CERN (The European Centre for Nuclear Research).

Weird Consequences of Space Flight

Various experiments have confirmed Einstein's mathematical prediction that the faster something travels relative to an observer (a reference point), the slower time passes for that "something", whether it be an atomic clock orbiting the Earth or astronauts in a spacecraft. Theory shows that time would slow down considerably as astronauts approached the speed of light. On interstellar flights they would age more slowly than the people back home. In this way relativity theory offers a way of travelling even across the Galaxy and back in a human lifetime, though many thousands of years would have passed on Earth. The slowing down of time at speeds near that of light would, therefore, seem to make return trips rather pointless, except for short journeys of, perhaps, a few light-years, for which the time differences might be acceptable.

Not the Way Ahead

The most powerful energy source today is nuclear fusion, displayed by the Sun, the stars and hydrogen bombs. Hydrogen combines to form helium, but less than one per cent of the matter involved in the reaction is released as energy. A little matter converts into an enormous amount of energy, as we know only too well from hydrogen bombs, but not enough energy to transport us swiftly to the stars. Let's say that we would like to travel at 99 per cent the speed of light. If we used a nuclear fusion rocket to make a return trip to Proxima Centauri, 4.5 light-years away, the fuel would weigh one billion times as much as the spaceship. (Proxima Centauri is the smallest star of a three-star system, one of which, Alpha Centauri, is like the Sun – see Fig. 8.1). We can reduce the amount of fuel if we travel at only one tenth the speed of light and collect all the fuel for the return journey when we reach Proxima Centauri. The weight of fuel at departure

Fig. 8.1: View from a planet orbiting Alpha Centauri A. This star system contains the three nearest stars to the Earth – Alpha Centauri A, Apha Centauri B and Proxima Centauri. The distance between A and B may be large enough to allow habitable planets to orbit these stars.

could then be reduced to a few hundred times the weight of the spaceship, though the round trip would take about 100 years.

Nuclear fusion, however, is less than one per cent efficient – only 0.7 per cent of matter is converted into energy. So let's consider the most efficient energy source theoretically possible: the matter-anti-matter reaction. Sub-atomic particles of matter and antimatter are frequently made to collide in giant accelerators during major experiments on the structure of matter. In this reaction all matter is transformed into energy. Yet even if antimatter could be produced in large quantities, and kept from contact with ordinary matter, it doesn't look like a practical source of energy for near speed-of-light space travel.

Let us imagine that a crewed spaceship, built in orbit, is propelled by matter-annihilation. It is accelerated to 99 per cent the speed of light on a voyage to the nearest star, Proxima Centauri. This is done at a rate that will provide a force equal to the Earth's gravity (1g) for the passengers. Slightly higher and the acceleration would be uncomfortable; much higher and it would kill the passengers. A spaceship accelerated to give a constant 1g would reach 99 per cent of the speed of light in six months. It would continue at that speed until six months before reaching its destination, when it would be decelerated to give 1g. The same procedure would have to be repeated on the return journey. The energy needed for these four manoeuvres, using a matter-antimatter reaction, would need a mass ratio of 40,000 to 1. In other words, the mass of the fuel would be 40,000 times that of the spaceship which would return to Earth orbit. All this energy, so carefully packaged for the journey, is dissipated into space. Is anyone anywhere going to use such a costly and impractical means of travelling to the stars? Don't forget, also, the cannon ball effects of the interstellar atoms and dust, which would continuously impact upon the spaceship. Heavy shielding would be needed, or energy would have to be used to create some kind of field with sufficient force to deflect interstellar particles, if such protection is possible when travelling at near the ultimate speed.

What kind of Crew?

At slower speeds much less fuel is needed and interstellar travel looks feasible, providing we can accept travel times of thousands of years. The ratio of energy to spaceship mass could be as low as 4:1, even using nuclear fusion as the energy source. For journeys lasting centuries (supposing human beings and not intelligent machines to be the travellers), large space colonies would be needed in which generations lived and died. The currently insoluble physical problems of energy and mass would then be replaced by biological and psychological problems, which could be even more difficult to solve. Could suitable people be found who would be prepared to leave their home planet in the Solar System to drift off into limitless space, never to return? Could space colonies maintain viable ecosystems more or less indefinitely?

Future Solutions

We can see in today's science the beginnings of research that might one day solve these problems, if they need to be solved in the future. Rather than having generations living and dying on board space colonies bound for nearby stars, we may find ways of allowing those present at departure to be present when the colony arrives at its destination. While space technologists and physicists publish papers on interstellar flight, biologists study the phenomenon of ageing, with the prospect of one day extending the human life span. Already the life spans of small mammals such as mice and rats can be doubled by no more than restricted feeding from birth. Biologists are also working on the biochemistry and physiology of hibernation, on suspending normal metabolism. So could a technique to extend the human life span considerably be linked with a method of hibernation for interstellar travellers?

There may, of course, be better solutions. Some biologists are looking at ways of breeding animals artificially from conception to birth, while people in computer technology are producing artificial intelligence and primitive mobile computers. Most experts in computer science accept that eventually something like a human level of intelligence may be produced artificially. Competent robots could then become as common as washing machines. No household would want to be without its robot. This development – because of the economic pressures to make better computer technology – could come before biologists can find ways of suspending animation or extending the human life span. Thus, given the availability of really intelligent robots, the hibernating or deep-freezing of human interstellar travellers looks like old-fashioned science fiction. With robots available, we could use what might be called 'terminal conception'. Deep-frozen sperm and ova would be packed aboard the spaceship so that their DNA could be combined when the time was right. The resulting human beings could then grow up and be educated in time for their arrival in the target planetary system, or when a suitable habitat had been built for them in orbit. This process would be managed by the robots, all the way from breeding and caring for the embryos to touchdown training. Suitably rational robots might make good parents for the first generation of a new civilization. A variation on this theme would be to have intelligent robots who could synthesise the genes necessary to produce that first generation. On the other hand, the robots, having done all the work, might decide to forget about the DNA of their human masters and establish a world fit for robots to live in. Anyway, those are the scenarios which may be possible one day, though in our time they do seem like science fiction.

Robots as Astronauts

Robots with the right mental attitude, as mobile as humans but more durable, could be the space travellers of advanced civilizations. Our robot servants (or maybe our masters, if things go wrong) could be ready for all tasks, and switch themselves off for long periods during travel time. The robots would depart, periodically reporting their discoveries – to Earth in our case. Hundreds of years later they might even return with specimens to fill the museums and astonish everyone.

If computer technologists and biologists achieve what most of them think is achievable, then interstellar travel and the exploration of the worlds of at least the nearest stars may become feasible in a century or so. Speed of light travel would not be needed, and virtually immortal computers of high intelligence could voyage through space for centuries, even millennia. They might or might not return, but the robots would be out there, continually gathering and transmitting new material to the home planet. Perhaps most advanced civilizations will have established such a system to gather information about its neighbourhood in the Galaxy. Once established, it could go on for ever.

A One-Way Trip to Alpha Centauri

Even today, without the breakthroughs in physics which may come during future centuries, we are offered the occasional ingenious plan to fly to the stars. The best way to span the light-years in the near future, using what we may call conventional means to catch a glimpse of our neighbouring planetary systems, is being planned with the proposed use of nanotechnology, technology which works using components of molecular dimensions.

"A spacecraft to Alpha Centauri, the nearest star to the Sun," said the headlines. This looked ambitious, especially as it was going to be dispatched "by the end of the century". It didn't say which century, but we can assume it meant this one. Further investigation revealed a project so ingenious that the spacecraft might actually go to Alpha Centauri by, well, the first decades of the next century.

Edward Belbruno and a team at the University of Minnesota plan to send a minute interstellar spacecraft which, they say, will weigh only a hundred grams. It will be driven into space by a beam of atomic particles fired at the spacecraft. The plan is to have a craft the shape of a wheel with micro-circuits, sensors and a capacity for recording images. A target plate would fill the centre of the wheel, which would be placed in Earth orbit. This target plate would then be struck by a beam of atomic particles shot from an accelerator which would also be in orbit. The beam would hit the target continuously for about four hours, involving some astounding accuracy since the wheel would be travelling faster than any spacecraft we have known. After four hours of blasting, the craft would be travelling at a third the speed of light and would reach Alpha Centauri in about 13 years. As the wheel is so light compared with the immense mass of Alpha Centauri, it could be pulled into an orbit, if it arrived at the right distance from the star. From orbit it could then observe any planets and transmit its findings. Data and images would take over four years to reach us.

Much research and development would be needed for this project. The type of accelerator currently available, a development from Star Wars, can fire its beam of atomic particles for only a second when four hours is needed, and the focusinging mechanism would cause a few headaches on its way to perfection. However, Belbruno maintains that all is possible within the next decade or two because the spacecraft will be nanotechnology, a rapidly developing technology, with individual components the size of large molecules. So this is one way to the stars. Make the spacecraft thousands of times smaller, and thousands of times less energy is needed to take them to their destinations. But the speed of light barrier remains for the impatient explorer. A 17-year-wait in Belbruno's case – and that's to look at the nearest star.

Exotic Travel

These scenarios will not match future reality if the nature of the universe offers better ways to cross the light-years. It is not unreasonable to expect that scientists during the next few hundred years will find some better solutions. It could be that none of the ways to the stars which we have considered will ever be used. New science may lead to more practical space technologies, but, for the present, the seeds of this new science lie in the imaginations.

Nevertheless, because current science cannot provide a practical solution, we must speculate on what future science may offer, even though it is only theory waiting for new findings from research. Using gravity to accelerate a spacecraft to its destination might become possible, if we could discover the nature of gravitational fields and in some way exploit this knowledge. Could we travel through space in a gravitational field which we would generate ourselves and deform in some way to steer us on our course? These two hypothetical methods for space travel have been considered by a few scientists who have studied the reported flight characteristics of some UFOs which seem to defy and manipulate the Earth's gravitational field. (There is no scientifically acceptable evidence that UFOs as spacecraft exist, but their reported flight characteristics have set a few minds in motion.) The strange thing is that thousands of UFO reports describe flight characteristics which are consistent with the hypothesis that gravitational fields are being used in some way; and there are no UFO reports from credible sources which describe any external mechanisms of propulsion.

Numerous physicists have speculated about by-passing the light-years by exploiting black holes and worm holes in space-time. They have even worked out how one might create worm holes before travelling through them. The point is that a worm hole, because of the deformation of space involved, might be a very short cut to far away places in the Galaxy. Physicists have also speculated about creating powerful gravitational fields around spacecraft. Given such a spacecraft for a trip across the Solar System, you might free yourself of the Earth's gravitational field, and, by manipulating your own field, let gravity from other bodies in the Solar System take you to wherever you wanted to go.

Another idea is to use the *strong force*, which operates within the atomic nucleus and holds all the particles of the nucleus securely together. This force, because of its great power if ever it could be used outside the nucleus, might be used to deform space-time. An interesting fact about the strong force is that it is opposite to the force of gravity in its effect. The strong force operates over the shortest distances imaginable within the atomic nucleus, but within its field it attracts particles more strongly as they move further apart. The strong force becomes stronger with distance, while the gravitational force becomes weaker with distance.

The problem with such speculation is that the strong force does not operate outside the nucleus. If it did operate beyond the nucleus, it would grab all orbiting electrons. There would then be no more atoms in the universe, only atomic nuclei. As Nobel laureate Steven Weinberg has said, "If the electrons in atoms and molecules felt the nuclear force, there would be no chemistry or crystallography or biology only physics." The universe as we know it would not be here.

Nevertheless, there are a few physicists on the fringe who have speculated that we might one day use the strong nuclear force in a propulsion system for interstellar travel. How we might get the strong force out of the atom and use it as an energy source in that way is beyond speculation.

The basic cause of our difficulties in seeing a future in space travel is that our current knowledge of physics is inadequate, and it is clear that a quantum leap in the technology of space travel can only come from research in physics. We might then travel in space within our own powerful gravitational field or we might so deform space-time between the Earth and our destination light-years away that little travel would be necessary. We would expand space-time between ourselves and the Earth so that it was greatly shortened between our spaceship and our destination. In this way we would not have to contradict Einstein because we wouldn't have to travel faster than light to bridge the light-years. Our spaceship could be more or less stationary with reference to an observer on Earth while space expanded behind us. This is all good speculative fun for a few theoretical physicists, but Nature may not offer a way of deforming space time. If Nature does, then any civilization thousands of years ahead of us in science and technology may already be using such a method for exploring the Galaxy.

Ideas from UFOs

It is intriguing to find that some unconventional ideas about the ultimate means of space flight have come from a few scientists, physicists and space engineers who have studied the reported flight characteristics of UFOs. It's probably safe to accept that if flying saucers are visiting us – and there is currently no scientifically acceptable proof that they are – the visitors would have developed the ultimate in space flight. Bear in mind that there are thousands of reports from all parts of the world: from airline pilots, the military and police, which describe with puzzling consistency certain flight characteristics. It could be that all these people are mistaken or hallucinating, but we can't be sure that this is so.

The first characteristic observed was that these craft, mostly measuring about 30 to 40 feet across and about 10 feet deep, seemed to be immune to the effects of gravity. No system of propulsion has been reported, yet these craft can outdistance any jet, and have done so, according to the military pilots who have been scrambled to investigate the intruders. No one who has not examined the relevant reports can appreciate the apparent authenticity of the reported events. A few scientists have, therefore, asked how such UFOs control their flight in the Earth's gravitational field. One clue to this is the way in which some saucers have consistently been reported to fly. They appear to be able to accelerate from a stationary position to speeds in excess of a thousand miles an hour within seconds. They are also reported to change direction, make right-angled turns, at high speeds. The g-forces of such manoeuvres would kill any human pilot, so how is the trick performed?

Certain scientists have suggested that the saucers in some way control the effects of gravity upon themselves by controlling their mass. This strikes a chord because particle physicists anticipate using their giant accelerators to find the Higgs boson, a large particle which, in the currently accepted theory of particle physics, bestows the quality of mass on matter.

Recently I received two official booklets on the work of CERN (The European Centre for Nuclear Research) in which it was stated that the discovery of the nature of mass was the main problem for physics today. You can see how seriously this problem is taken by the amounts of money spent to find a solution. The Large Hadron Collider at CERN, which cost £1.5 billion, supplied by the European nations involved, will search for the Higgs boson. It will be its main future research task.

We take for granted in everyday life that matter and mass and inertia (the resistance of mass to be moved) are all inseparably locked together, but in reality they are three separate physical qualities. It may be possible when we know more about matter at a sub-nuclear level (when we know how the quality of mass is bestowed upon matter) to nullify the quality of mass. Remove most of the mass from your spacecraft (though none of the matter) and at the same time you would remove most of its inertia. With negligible inertia you could take right-angled turns at great speed, but you would have to be careful about removing your mass. Remove all the mass, so that the spacecraft and everything inside are massless, and you would immediately travel away at the speed of light. All massless entities travel at the speed of light in this universe. So, do any of those thousands of UFO reports describe spacecraft? If they do, then ET has solved the problem of space flight and some of those reports warrant scientific investigation.

Negative Matter

Negative matter is another speculative offering from some of the more imaginative physicists, including Robert Forward in the United States. The distinguished theoretical physicist, Sir Hermann Bondi, published a paper on the subject as long ago as 1957. Other mathematical physicists later confirmed that negative matter fitted satisfactorily into the theoretical framework of contemporary physics.

It's important to note that we are not talking here about antimatter which does exist in the accelerators of particle physics, and annihilates itself and an equal quantity of ordinary matter on contact, when all the matter involved is transformed into energy. In antimatter, all the atomic particles have charges opposite to those in ordinary matter. This is not so with negative matter. The main difference with negative matter is that it responds in an opposite way to ordinary matter in a gravitational field. Drop a chunk of negative matter and it will fly into space with increasing velocity.

"I have tried to find some law of physics or some rule of logic that would forbid the existence of negative matter," wrote Robert Forward. "I have found none." It is an all important point to note that, according to the laws of physics, the gravitational field of a chunk of negative matter would repel all matter. It would repel both positive matter (ordinary matter) and negative matter, even though the gravitational field of positive matter would attract negative matter. (Since that apple fell on Newton's head, we've known, of course, that positive matter attracts positive matter.)

This relationship between positive matter and negative matter is,

Fig. 8.2: One of the possible ultimate systems for space propulsion. The theoretical physics of this system may seem a little odd. While the gravitational field of negative matter would repel positive (normal) matter, positive matter would attract negative matter.

therefore, a wonderful gift from the laws of the universe, if only we could obtain some negative matter. An arrangement like that shown in Fig. 8.2 could accelerate us to the stars without the need of fuel – no combustion or reaction rockets needed. Even the antimatter drives of "Star Trek" would become technological antiques. Engineers would invent a vast array of technologies based on the free energy which negative mass and the force of gravity would freely provide.

Negative mass would, therefore, be a rather valuable commodity. Robert Forward thinks that there are some vague clues that negative matter exists out there in space. "There is always the small, faint hope that negative matter is not forbidden," he says, "and that a properly designed search will lead to its discovery."

We come back here to what could be the hard reality of ceilings considered in Chapter 3. Are we about to bump our heads on the ceiling of Nature's secrets, or is the ceiling to knowledge high enough to allow the existence of the phenomenon of negative matter, or something equally useful? They would enable us to develop those future technological marvels, including that wonderful space technology that would take advanced civilizations to the stars.

Chapter Nine

Looking for Alien Probes

I t would be strange indeed if the human race did not find some way of exploring other planetary systems. What is the sense in astronomers searching for evidence that planets exist in orbit about our neighbouring stars, if the space technologists don't eventually follow this with space probes to obtain a closer look? Other stars and their planets are prospective wonders too intriguing for us to neglect. We may assume, therefore, that any space-faring civilizations with the space technology to do so will have explored other planetary systems, given that interstellar space can be crossed. But what would have been the main way of carrying out such explorations?

The interstellar equivalent of today's unmanned, interplanetary probes would surely be the first stage of such planetary exploration, and it might be the only stage for routine explorations if interstellar space is very difficult and dangerous to cross. We have no available means (or resources) to dispatch such craft to the stars, but space technologists have already spent much time thinking about them – and even designing them in detail, although the building of their creations must await the development of future science and technology. Nevertheless, we may be within a century of a busy interstellar-probe business.

We look here at what our civilization may do in the near future in order to guess what others may have already done during the past few billion years. If the scenario which includes the evolution of Earth-like planets and intelligent life throughout the Galaxy is correct, then there is a chance that probes from elsewhere have entered the Solar System sometime in the past. If so, they might still be here and we could obtain evidence of ETs through finding these probes, or artefacts that the probes have left behind. It's reasonable to accept that the probes of civilizations thousands or millions of years more advanced than ourselves might be very different from the probes we sent to study the worlds of the Solar System. We might not even recognise ET's interstellar probes as such if evidence of one were before us.

Patient Probes

It was Ronald N. Bracewell, a professor of Electrical Engineering at Stanford University, who suggested in 1960 the possibility of receiving radio transmissions from interstellar probes. Since then, other writers have elaborated upon this idea. Bracewell suggested that an alien probe might enter a planetary system and go into an orbit in the habitable zone, the zone in which constant physical conditions (provided by the right amount of heat from the planet's sun) would enable an Earth-like planet to support life continuously for several billion years. From such an orbit, said Bracewell, the probe would be able to pick up any intelligent signals, such as our radio and television broadcasts which are continually leaking into space. The probe would then know that a technological civilization was in residence and it could respond to the signals. One objection to this scenario is that for most probes there would be no broadcasts from any planets. What then? Bracewell suggested that in this case a probe might wait in orbit, perhaps for several million years, until it was stimulated to action by the first radio transmissions of an emerging civilization.

My feeling is that probes with this sort of patience would not be built, simply because they would have little chance of success. An intelligent probe would know that a stay in orbital hibernation would almost certainly be permanent if it waited for the invention of broadcasting. Consider: it has taken four billion years (since the origin of life) for the first broadcasts to be made in the Solar System, and the period of time during which we will continue to leak radio and television transmissions into space is unknown. Although ETs may launch probes to explore other planetary systems, as we do to study the worlds of the Solar System, they can hardly expect their probes to detect broadcasts.

Of course, we have unintentionally sent radio transmissions into space for the past 75 years, which means that the first of these are now 75 light-years away from Earth. Conceivably, ETs might detect our broadcasting and send probes. The Earth's brightness in natural radio waves is between 210 and 290 Kelvin. That's not very bright. But at certain wavelengths the Earth radiates at a million degrees. It outshines the Sun in these wavelengths and could be detected even by our current radio telescopes at a distance of ten light-years. Consequently, any ET probe at present near the Solar System should be able to detect us. It seems more likely, however, that the interstellar probes of other world civilizations, if such exist within fifty or so light-years, will have been launched because of the ozone and oxygen lines in the spectrum of radiation which our atmosphere has been radiating into space for at least the past 350 million years, since our atmosphere reached a comparable level in its oxygen content to what exists today. As we saw in Chapter 4, astronomers are currently working on designs for the detection of these spectral lines from any nearby planetary systems which may be discovered. All they need to enter this area of research is enough money and a slightly more advanced space programme. If advanced ETs are out there within, say, fifty light-years, they could have detected the biosphere of Earth at any time during the past 350 million years, mainly from the prominent spectral line of ozone. The ET astronomers would have then known that they were observing a planet with a rich oxygen atmosphere and abundant life (since life has created our oxygen atmosphere). Any civilization with the appropriate space technology would have wanted to explore further. Blue planets (Earth-like planets) must be the most interesting places in the universe, whether they have technologists in residence or not.

Presumably we would follow this path of exploration, given the technological opportunity to do so, for as long as the present inquisitive stage of our civilization lasts. But are advanced civilizations going to send probes just to have them wait in orbit? Any arriving here during the Earth's first four billion years would have had a long wait. The chance of a probe finding broadcasters in residence is too remote. It's not a realistic expectation. Can we expect ETs to leave their probes in alien planetary systems, waiting for the primitive inhabitants to wake up and invent radio?

Perfect Probes

Like every other technology, there seems no reason why interstellar probes should not be developed to their 'limit of technical perfectibility'. Even the first interstellar probes are, however, unlikely to resemble Daedalus, the probe designed in 1977 by scientists and engineers of the British Interplanetary Society. Daedalus is a probe designed to go to just one nearby star, sent on its way by a controlled series of hydrogen bomb explosions. Yet after such trouble and expense it would fly straight through any planetary system that might be present. There would be no attempt to decrease its speed (one-tenth the speed of light) or manoeuvre it in any way – there wouldn't be enough energy left to do so. Could anyone believe that such a costly and impractical probe would ever move from the drawing board?

Unimaginable Probes

The successes achieved by NASA and the old Soviet Union with space probes within the Solar System tempted us to think that probes could soon be sent to the stars. The problem is that the nearest stars are millions of times further away than Mars or Venus. Chemical rockets are just about adequate to propel small spacecraft to the worlds of the Solar System, but totally inadequate for trips to the stars. We need a system to propel space probes on their way at speeds approaching that of light, if we are going to receive information from them within the human life span. That system of propulsion does not yet exist. We do not even know if physicists can discover the science needed to develop a near-speed-of-light space technology, though we must, for the present, assume that the knowledge does exist in Nature. If it doesn't, then only intelligent species with life spans of thousands of years, if any there be, are likely to invest in interplanetary probes.

For our purposes we have to assume that the knowledge exists in Nature for the development of adequately speedy probes and also, perhaps, for very long-lived ETs. If we do not assume this much, there is no point in searching for probes in the Solar System. Having said that, we have to admit that we really don't know what we are looking for. Our current ideas about what an interstellar probe might be could be far from reality. If such probes have a reality they will be the product of beings at least thousands of years more advanced than ourselves.

Photographic Search

Two astronomers, Robert Freitas and Francisco Valdes, have looked for evidence of alien probes using optical telescopes. First, in 1979 at the Leuschner Observatory, University of California, Berkeley, they searched the stable orbits about the Lagrangian points L4 and L5 of

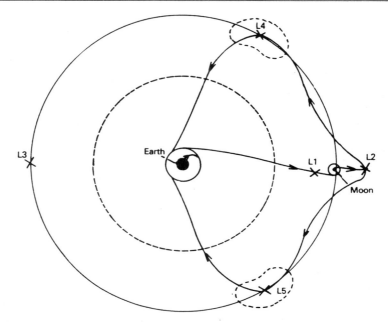

Fig 9.1: The five Lagrangian points of the Earth-Moon gravitational system. L4 and L5 provide stable orbits. The inner circle represents a geosynchronous orbit; the outer circle the Moon's orbit. The dashed circle is thought to be a suitable orbit for future space colonies.

the Earth-Moon gravitational system and took 90 photographic plates (see Fig. 9.1).

Five Lagrangian points exist in the gravitational field of a two-body system, such as the Earth and Moon. A third body, placed at any of these L-points, will stay there permanently in space. In the case of the Earth-Moon system, the Sun's gravitation would make any object placed near L4 or L5 orbit the L-point slowly, once every 89 days. The Lagrangian points would, therefore, offer ideal parking places for alien probes.

In 1981-82, Freitas and Valdes tried again without success. They searched all five of the Earth-Moon L-points and L1 and L2 of the Sun-Earth system, using the 24-inch (0.61 m) telescope at the Kitt Peak Observatory in Arizona. They took 137 photographic plates which, at best, would have shown artefacts as small as a few metres in size. Although no probes were found, the reasons for searching are as good as the reasons for searching for radio signals from other worlds. We can reasonably assume that civilizations sufficiently advanced to transmit their messages for thousands of years might also have the technology needed to dispatch probes to neighbouring planetary systems which they know to exist from their astronomy. They might never receive replies to their radio messages, but their own probes, if successful, would be certain to send back a wealth of interesting information.

Therefore, given that space-faring civilizations have been evolving in our Galaxy during the past several billion years, it would seem possible that a few alien probes, if not the actual extraterrestrial s themselves, have at some time entered the Solar System. My guess is that the probe makers would remain comfortably at home with their intellectual pursuits, while the artificial intelligences (robots) went for them, crossing the perpetual night of interstellar space to discover for them the wonders of other worlds.

Hidden Probes

Most people assume that an alien probe in nearby space would be quickly detected. This is not so. Robert Freitas presents us with a few figures to show just how vast the search area could be, "A sphere with the radius of the Solar System out to the orbit of Pluto consists of 260,000 cubic astronomical units (an AU is the mean Sun-Earth distance). The surfaces of planets, moons and asteroids provide 100,000 million square kilometres. Even if the best telescope on Earth was employed exclusively to look for alien artefacts it could scan only one-millionth of the necessary volume. Orbital space is at least 99.999 per cent unexplored for 1-10 metre objects. Of the 100,000,000,000 square kilometres of Solar System territory outside the Earth, less than 50 million has been examined down to a resolution of 1 to 10 metres, so that 99.95 per cent is still virgin territory. Even huge 1-10 kilometre artificial alien habitats in the Asteroid Belt would be visually indistinguishable from asteroids to terrestrial observers."

Nevertheless, despite these difficulties, we can calculate the best places to park an alien probe within these vast regions of space and land. The L-orbits so far searched are some of these.

Freitas offers two criteria for sites:

¤   "Ability to consistently monitor environments most likely to harbour or evolve intelligent life.

¤   Maximum artefact life span with minimum complexity."

When one takes these criteria into account, the volume of space that it may be profitable to search is greatly reduced. "The potential search volume," says Freitas, "thus reduces to five distinct orbital classes, all of which are poorly studied for 1-10 metre objects.

These are:

¤ Geocentric orbits between two Earth-centred concentric spheres of radii 70,000 and 326,400 km.

¤ Moon-centred orbits between 3,000 and 58,100 km lunar altitude.

¤ Stable orbits around Earth-Moon Lagrangian points L4 and L5.

¤ Earth-Moon system orbits near Lagrangian points L1 and L2.

¤ Sun-Earth Lagrangian orbits L4 and L5."

We could speculate (rather freely) that if an advanced probe arrived during the past million years or so, it might have stayed if it detected the emergence of a technological species. This could be a very rare event for a probe, a phenomenon worthy of further observation. Early Homo sapiens were roaming about 250,000 years ago, though perhaps rather dim-witted and bony-browed and not doing a great deal to attract the attentions of an advanced probe or ET visitor. But once civilization began to develop, some ten thousand years ago, the evidence that intelligent activity was underway on Earth would have been unmistakable. So the past ten thousand years of human activity might have been irresistibly interesting to any ETs that might have noticed what was going on, especially if new emerging civilizations are rare events, as we can suppose they must be, given that it has taken four billion years on Earth for ours to emerge.

Probe Economics

We are unlikely to launch large numbers of interstellar probes in the foreseeable future because of their cost. Until we can create the robots that would do the manufacturing of space probes for us, preferably in space along with most of our other major manufacturing industries of the future, probes would be an expensive way of exploring other planetary systems. And as a way of discovering alien intelligences would be quite beyond us for a few centuries. Advanced ETs, however, might be in a position to launch probes in their thousands, so that they might be the primary way of detecting intelligence in other planetary systems. Probes reaching other planetary systems would be sure to discover many things of great interest, even where no life existed, and the discovery of intelligent life might be regarded as a rare bonus, which could then be continuously monitored for future developments.

John H. Wolfe, when at the SETI Program Office at Ames Research Center in California, reviewed the subject of probes in NASA's SETI report SF-419. He accepted that we may send a few probes to nearby stars but wrote, "To 'bug' all the sun-like stars within 1,000 light-years would require about 1,000,000 probes. If we launched one a day this would take 3,000 years and an overall expenditure of 10 trillion dollars. Interstellar probes are appealing as long as someone else sends them, but not when we face the task ourselves."

The point here is that it would cost us too much now, but would John Wolfe's counterpart in the 30th century be saying the same thing. By that time robots may make as many probes as we need.

Thus the probability that probes have entered the Solar System may not be low if probes at their 'level of perfectibility' have the capacity to make copies of themselves and redirect them to other planetary systems. I.R. Cameron has estimated ('Scientific American', July 1973) that the erosion rate of meteorites in the Solar System is between 0.2 mm and 1 cm per million years, depending on the materials composing the meteorites. We could, therefore, expect a specially constructed probe to wear better than the hardest meteorite, so that probes may survive in space for many millions of years. The lifetime of the functional parts within the probe would depend on how technically perfect they were. We cannot guess about this, but whatever could be achieved would probably be achieved by those ETs involved in the launching of interstellar probes. We can imagine interstellar probes being made and dispatched automatically, perhaps from asteroids in the home planetary system. A civilization 1,000 years ahead of us technically might do this with no more difficulty than we mass produce automobiles. No more attention may then be needed than to check that the robots are behaving themselves and that the probe assembly plant is functioning properly. Beyond that, all the master minds need to do is to study the data from the probes in other planetary systems.

A Longer Life Span

ETIs would need plenty of time to participate in such a venture. A hundred years or more might pass before a probe reached its first target star, though once an interstellar probe project was under way

– say after about the first few hundred years – a steady flow of data could keep interest alive back home. Consequently, the time needed might not deter a long-lived species. Even we might take up this challenge one day. Once the 'death program' in human genes can be rewritten by advanced molecular engineering into a 'life program', we may live hundreds of years in a youthful condition. Barring accidents, we might survive indefinitely and be well able to participate in research projects lasting thousands of years, though for this to be possible most people would be living in space colonies within the Solar System. Life in space colonies, as envisaged and designed by the late Professor Gerard O'Neill, could be pleasant and the climate and environment could be changed to suit the inhabitants' preferences. On Earth most of us have little choice about the environment and climate we live in.

Incidentally, an increased longevity could be one more reason for advanced societies to colonize space. This, added to demands for more energy and more technology, could be too much for any civilization bound to a planetary surface. Yet once we gain control of our genes, a longer life span should be a real possibility. We can even speculate how this might be done by switching off a gene here and there. Whereas we can't speculate much about 'faster than light' travel because the answer to it, if there is one, lies deep within fundamental physics, arguably the most difficult, and certainly the most abstract, area of science.

Molecules bind us to Earth

What could be more interesting for our descendants, in their eternal youth, than to explore the wonders of our galactic neighbourhood? Exactly the same can be said for the other technological species which we have to speculate upon. But probes and robotic missions may offer the only practical way to explore other worlds. The distinctive nature of each planetary biosphere – because each will have evolved from a molecular level in complete isolation – may make extraterrestrial visits by biological beings impossibly difficult. The molecular structures and machinery of life on Earth, and the ways in which organisms have evolved to deal with them may place important limitations on space travel. The literature of science fiction has failed to recognise this major obstacle to visiting aliens, or future human astronauts bravely going forth to explore new worlds. The stories of aliens who embark from flying saucers to tell us nothing in particular equally ignore the biological problems of such visits. To survive here the reported occupants of flying saucers would have to be Earthly primates or robots free from the need for food, and also immune from biological attack by our abundant micro-organisms. We cannot expect the proteins that we use to rebuild our bodies and supply the enzymes for our metabolism to be suitable for visitors. Our food would, therefore, wreck the metabolism of any visiting alien whose molecular base was even slightly different. The same would go for future Captain Kirks feasting on strange new worlds. So, no food for aliens, but abundant micro-organisms which would end their days as soon as they set an unprotected foot on Earth.

The colonization of life-bearing planets throughout the Galaxy, so much envisaged in science fiction, is not at all practical, even given that advanced civilizations can cross the light-years with relative ease. We often hear speculation from scientists, who should know better, that humankind will one day colonize other planetary systems. If such colonization does take place, then it will have to be of sterile worlds. An alien biosphere would be no place for us to set up home, but that does not mean that other world civilizations have not explored planetary systems beyond their own, including the Solar System. The time available is incomprehensible to us and favours the probability of such activity at some period in the past. It does not favour the probability of ET visits in our particular epoch, unless intelligent life-forms are abundant in our part of the Galaxy, or unless our presence was discovered long ago and we are now being monitored. A new planetary civilization, for statistical reasons, is going to be a rare phenomenon deserving special attention.

For this and other reasons we should, perhaps, keep our scientific eyes open and avoid preconceptions, since we can only guess what the situation is out there. In order to deny the possibility of ET activity within the Solar System at some time, whether we are able to detect it or not, we have to put forward negative hypotheses on the origin of Earth-like planets, life, intelligence and interstellar space flight, none of which can be tested in our present state of knowledge. On the other hand, we can test the ETH (ExtraTerrestrial Hypothesis). Negative hypotheses are therefore dead-end thinking for us.

The untestable hypotheses are:

¤ Alien astronomy and interstellar travel (at least by small intelligent space probes) has never been pursued during the past 3 to 4 billion years to a level which would lead to the discovery of the Solar System.

¤   The origin of life on Earth is unique, or an event so rare that few
    life-forms have ever evolved with intelligence capable of creating
    advanced technology.

¤   The distances in time and space separating technological worlds
    are too great ever to be crossed. No better way of interstellar travel
    will ever be invented than those which we can presently envisage.
    There is no new science to be discovered that will make journeys
    to the stars possible.

¤   Although the origin of life is not a rare event in itself, given
    appropriate planetary conditions, the evolution of technological
    intelligence is very rare. We note here its uniqueness on this
    planet, a point which is frequently made, although many intelli-
    gent animals have evolved and would have continued to evolve,
    perhaps becoming more intelligent, had humankind not become
    dominant.

¤   All advanced technological civilizations become extinct because
    of the adverse factors they create. None, or very few, survive the
    first technological bonanza, so none, or very few, go on to develop
    the technology of interstellar space flight to the routine level
    needed to explore other planetary systems and other life in the
    Galaxy.

As we cannot test any of these hypotheses, it is potentially more
profitable to focus on hypotheses that we can test, such as the ETH.
Finding different ways to test it is difficult, and we should welcome
any realistic opportunity to do so.

Chapter Ten

The Colonization Factor

The Russian visionary Konstantin Tsiolkovskii, an ardent advocate for the hypothesis of the plurality of inhabited worlds, wrote, "Is it possible that Europe is inhabited and other parts of the world are not?" It was a rhetorical question put to evoke a definite "no" from his readers, but on reflection a qualified "yes" is also a valid answer. Yes, it would have been possible for other parts of the world to be uninhabited had there been barriers that could not be crossed. Indeed, many parts of the world were without human habitation until recent times, when it became possible to cross some ocean barriers. Though humans had lived in Asia for thousands of years, none crossed the sea to neighbouring Australia until about 50,000 years ago, when the first aborigines entered the continent. Even in historical times, between about 1000 BC and 1000 AD, the Polynesians crossed the Pacific Ocean in their big canoes, hopping from island to island over the generations. They populated, for the first time, the islands of Samoa, Tonga, Hawaii, Easter Island and New Zealand, taking their culture and edible plants with them.

It seems probable (because our galaxy contains a few billion stars like the Sun) that biospheres as rich in their variety of life-forms as ours have evolved on many planets. The processes that have formed our biosphere appear inherent in the evolution of planets which, like the Earth, meet a very demanding set of conditions. Such planets may, of course, be rare, and creatures with technological intelligence may not often evolve, even in the most flourishing biosphere. Millions of animal species have evolved on Earth, yet only one line has led to technological intelligence.

We therefore have to allow for the possibility that any widespread presence of civilizations in a galaxy may be due more to interstellar travel than to each biosphere of an Earth-type planet producing its own unique technological species. Yet there are apparently insurmountable biological obstacles to such colonization. The colonization of the Galaxy does not have an analogy in the colonization of the Pacific Islands by the Polynesians during two thousand years of island hopping. Yet certain physicists and astronomers have offered this analogy to show that the Galaxy should have been colonized by now, if the ETs are out there – and ETs, if they exist, should be a familiar sight in our daily lives.

The objection to this line of thought lies in the biological implications of trying to colonize planets with a biosphere similar to that of the Earth. They would be the most unsuitable places for any aliens to inhabit. ETs from different planetary systems may have visited the Solar System during the past few hundred million years, but would they have wanted to set up home on Earth? For them – if they were biological beings like ourselves – the Earth, with its vast supply of micro-organisms, would be the most dangerous place in the Solar System. There would be nothing for them to eat because the amino acid molecules which form our proteins, and other molecules essential for the metabolisms of life on Earth, would be at least slightly alien to them. They wouldn't use the same group of twenty amino acids that we use to build our proteins. The structures within our cells and our genetic code, which assembles those amino acid molecules in the right sequences to manufacture the proteins needed to build bodies, are not going to be duplicated in an alien biosphere. Our genetic code has evolved here and all life on Earth uses it. And, as is the nature of codes, it is very complicated. For a visiting alien to have the same genetic code as ourselves would be impossible.

The biological hazards in another biosphere would be everywhere, and mostly invisible. Looked at from our point of view, the alien equivalent of our viruses should not be a problem because viruses evolve for specific hosts. Few animal or plant viruses will affect us and vice versa. The equivalent of our bacteria and many other types of micro-organisms could, however, be catastrophic for our health and survival on another Earth-like planet. Biological aliens are therefore not going to subject themselves to such dangers on this planet. And we can reasonably speculate that any colonization of the Galaxy is going to exclude the take over of planets with biospheres – at least by biological beings. Non-biological beings would pose an awkward problem which we will consider shortly.

It is ironic that the major scientific critics of astronomical SETI, including physics and astronomy professors Frank Tipler, John Barrow and Michael Hart, have generated so much controversy in the

scientific press by omitting these biological reasons against colonization in their otherwise excellent papers. They claim that ETs do not
exist because if they did they would be walking arm in arm down the
high street. Frank Tipler, for example, uses the colonization of the
South Sea Islands by the Polynesians as a precise analogy for the
colonization of planetary systems throughout the Galaxy, when there
is no analogy here at all. Colonization by an enterprising species
within one biosphere is quiet different from any hypothetical colonization of a wide range of different planetary biospheres, even if it is
possible to cross several light-years (the average distance between the
stars) and transport all one needs with relative ease.

It is also difficult to see how any super civilization would benefit
from colonizing a large number of other planetary systems. Perhaps
just a few to insure against catastrophes and extinction would be
enough. Exploration of other worlds would be an entirely different
business. Advanced societies might wish to explore and study as
many other planetary systems as they could. We would like to do
that, but we wouldn't want to destroy our objects of study by colonizing them.

Custom-Made Worlds

It has been suggested that civilizations could build miniature worlds
with their own chosen environments in order to travel from star to
star. In theory, in this way it might be possible to settle in planetary
systems where planets like the Earth exist, or in systems where no
technological intelligence or even any form of life could ever evolve.
It is difficult to see how civilizations, having settled in other planetary
systems in this way, could ever become extinct. Immortality may,
therefore, lie in the technology of interstellar space flight. Though
civilizations and their citizens would continue to evolve wherever
they were in the Galaxy, the precarious existence of advanced technological civilizations that stay put on one planet might be avoided.
Already we can see the wisdom of putting some of our eggs into
another basket by building space colonies in nearby space which
could survive any catastrophes on Earth. Clearly, the longer we keep
all our eggs on Earth, the more precarious our future becomes. It's
little consolation to know that if we do subject ourselves to the
ultimate catastrophe, there might still be time for a second coming of
advanced life before the Sun dies. Current astronomical theory pre-
dicts that within another billion years the Sun will make the Earth

too hot for life. Heat-loving bacteria would be the last organisms to survive. Bacteria were the first inhabitants of Earth and will be the last.

Technology and Conservation

An advanced space technology would therefore offer humanity more than an insurance policy – the only one, perhaps, that we are still capable of having. It is possible that we may have to claim on that policy within a few hundred years rather than a billion years. Humanity has become locked into an advancing science and technology that may make the establishment and development of space colonies a necessity. But we will need a revolutionary new system of space propulsion to enter a space age in which we could establish space colonies, and the fundamental physics that might make the new propulsion system possible has yet to be discovered. Without this development, which only the physicists can give us, our civilization may end in wars over diminishing resources and overcrowded territory as populations grow. A 'limits to growth' policy, so widely publicised in recent years, may delay the inevitable disasters, but it cannot be a long-term solution because it goes directly against the basic nature of our species which we cannot expect to overcome in the short-term. The ancient drive for expansion is sealed within our genes. It ensured survival and dominance in a world ripe for exploitation. Can we go into reverse now? Although the first space colony will be very expensive, it is an option that will be bought if we have the technology available and are not stopped by catastrophes on Earth.

The envisaged colonization of nearby space as an international venture (involving all the expertise of scientists in the United States, Russia, Europe and Asia) is a rational technological development, but it can never be undertaken with current chemical rocketry. Therefore, unless we are all going to become very green in our attitude to the environment, the future of humanity seems to rest with the physicists and space technologists. The initial justification for supporting their research could be that it would help meet our increasing demands for energy without posing a threat to the environment.

Gerard O'Neill, who did the relevant calculations years ago, used to make the point that if we colonized the Moon and Mars, as has often been envisaged, we could only double our living space. By mining the Moon and using the asteroids to build space colonies, our living area could be increased 3,000 times. Anyway, the Moon and Mars are not really suitable for colonization, no matter what the enthusiasts for terraforming Mars may say. The Moon's night is fourteen Earth days long, and its low gravity – and that of Mars – would make permanent colonization difficult. For one thing, children born and reared on either of these worlds would probably grow abnormally tall because of the low gravity. Who would want twelve-feet-tall children who could never return to Earth without collapsing under the force of 1g? Even people born and breed on Earth might not be able to re-adapt to 1g after living for years on the Moon or Mars. Large space colonies may look like science fiction at present, but they could at least provide a 1g environment by turning on their axes at the appropriate rate. Far more difficult would be the need to maintain viable biospheres in space colonies isolated from Earth. The biology involved could be much more difficult to control than the space engineering.

The Way into Space

In the BBC's 'Radio Times' for 9th September 1980, under the heading 'The Grand Experiment', I read, "This is the most absurd scheme that ever entered the head of man to conceive." The writer lived in the early years of the 19th century and he was criticizing the plan to build a railway system in Britain. Likewise, some present-day critics have condemned the plans to build space colonies, though we are farther from this enterprise than our critic was from the building of railways.

The first steps towards space colonization (Gerard O'Neill liked to call it the 'humanisation of space') have been planned in detail for some 25 years. The first colony could follow logically from the space stations that will be built in orbit, but only if a new and practical system of space propulsion can be developed. The transportation of what would be needed to build the first colony would not otherwise be practical. There have been conferences on space colony technology, mainly at Princeton University, and study sessions at NASA's Ames Research Center. NASA has supported work on the technology, and aerospace industries have entered the field.

The enthusiasts for space colonies justify the cost of the first colony on the capability of its inhabitants to build and service solar satellites in space. Solar satellites are large and heavy and would be expensive to launch from Earth, although one solar satellite could provide 10,000 megawatts, enough power for a large city. Sunlight in orbit is four times greater in intensity than that falling on the sunniest region of Earth. This undiluted energy, which exists in space for collection twenty-four hours a day, would be transmitted to Earth in the form of microwaves – and received, presumably, in very isolated parts of the planet.

We might think that by the time a space colony could be established to build and service solar satellites, the technology of controlled nuclear fusion would be providing unlimited energy. The scientists who advocate solar satellites say that this may not be so. Nuclear fusion technology, they believe, may take much longer to develop than anticipated. Those in fusion research cannot say how long it will take. Estimates of several decades are given, but the technology, after vast sums of money have been spent on it, is still at an early experimental stage.

Meanwhile, the damage from pollution increases, and one wonders for how long humanity can continue to raise its material standards without taking industry and other energy consuming activities into space. There seems no long-term alternative, except that of restricting technological development and material living standards. This problem might be encountered by other expanding technological civilizations, so that the establishment of space colonies within planetary systems might be a common phenomenon.

On Earth we are in a sort of 'gravitational hole' out of which we have to climb before we can go anywhere. The energy needed to move one astronaut, or a passenger, into orbit is equal to the energy one person would use climbing out of a hole 4,000 miles deep. The development of a system of space propulsion which overcame this problem, and led to the building of space colonies, could lead to an advance for humanity equal in significance to the advance made by life when it colonized dry land, after spending its previous history confined to the seas and rivers of the world. It is a development that could be universal for successful technological species – which is, of course, why we are considering it here, given that physicists of other worlds have already provided the knowledge needed to develop a practical means of space travel.

First Space Colony

The idea of space colonies is not new. Some bold imaginations thought of them more than 50 years ago, when what they envisaged appeared no more than fantasy, and was indeed fantasy at the time.

O'Neill's contribution lies in showing that space colonies are technically possible, though he was a little premature in thinking that they would be economically possible in the very near future. Nowadays, it seems that the dreams of fifty years ago (and the carefully calculated schemes of O'Neill) can only become reality when a new level of space flight technology has been developed.

O'Neill first considered space colonies with his physics students at Princeton in 1969. He asked them, "Is a planetary surface the right place for an expanding technological civilization?" The answer they came up with was a most emphatic "No". Many talented people subsequently studied the same question and reached the same conclusion. The key to this development would be the first space colony, "Island One". Once the inhabitants had paid for their mission by building, launching and maintaining solar satellites, or some other useful space work, the rest would be a bonus.

Space colonization could become self-supporting and self-perpetuating. More colonies could be built until millions of people lived permanently in space, where they might even have a more interesting life than on Earth. That's the theory, which rests on two things: the availability of economical space flight and the ability to maintain permanent stable biospheres in the space colonies, a subject which has attracted much attention in recent years. Besides supplying electricity and manufactured goods, the colonies would grow their own food, being able to produce any type of climate they wanted by suitably orienting their colony (see Figs 10.1 and 10.2). Science, too, would move into a new era of research. Astronomers would set up observatories near colonies rather than on the Earth, using new techniques to study the universe – and, possibly, to detect any ET signals.

Ecosystems in Space

The main problems could come from trying to establish stable ecosystems. Normally, on Earth, even a tiny habitat contains a countless number of different organisms living in a state of dynamic equilibrium. Stable ecosystems establish themselves on Earth through a succession of communities of animals and plants, usually over very long periods of time. The type of stable ecosystem depends on physical factors such as temperature, rainfall and nature of the soil. In theory, colonists could control these factors, so giving themselves whatever kind of ecosystem they wanted, but establishing the desired

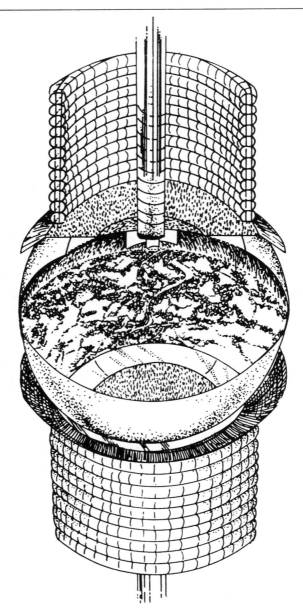

Fig. 10.1: Cutaway view of Island One which would rotate twice a minute to give a maximum gravity of 1g. The axial cylinder is an air passage with a corridor for the docking of spacecraft and an area for industries that have to be conducted in zero gravity; the regions above and below the sphere would be used for farming

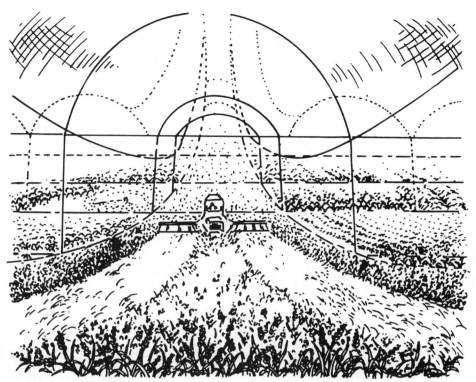

Fig. 10.2: Multiple-wheel geometry would be used for farming in Island One.

ecosystem might take a long time. We can imagine new space colonies being uninhabited except for a few ecologists, attending to the appropriate plants, animals and saprophytes (the fungi and bacteria, the indispensable scavengers of nature in life's recycling processes). All would be growing into specified ecosystems, temperate or sub-tropical, for example, before full human habitation. That is how natural ecosystems would have to be established. The alternative would be a great deal of gardening and control systems to maintain biological stability. As the largest envisaged colony, Island Three, would have a living area of 500 square miles, this could involve a lot of gardeners.

The argument that space colonies offer the only way to accommodate continued human expansion rests on the fact that we are a species born and bred to expansion. We have grown to need freedom from constraints on at least some technological fronts. Technological growth must otherwise soon be rigidly curtailed in a civilization bound to the Earth. We either go into space or our species must permanently inhabit a small, closed system in space and time, evolving in isolation, either quickly or slowly, to extinction.

If we returned to Earth in two or three centuries, would we find that several generations of humans had built thousands of space colonies, many of which could be observed in the night sky? It could be so. O'Neill calculated that our technological growth, just within the Solar System, could continue unhindered in this way for another 5,000 years, given that the increase in the population was no more than 15 per cent during a human lifetime. The human population would then be some 20,000 times its present size.

Consequently, some space scientists accept that more people will one day live in space colonies than live on Earth. To them it seems the only workable solution to our present problems. If this is so, it follows that other intelligent species in time and space may have found this solution when faced with similar problems.

We may therefore speculate that any interstellar travellers who visited the Solar System in the past would have been familiar with the "space colony" business, and would not have established themselves on Earth for two main reasons. Firstly, they would have to live permanently with ever-present biological threats to their safety. Bacteria and other micro-organisms which are everywhere in the environment could make visits to the Earth's surface impossible for an alien species without suitable protection. Secondly, they would be better able to carry on their technological activities in space colonies. They might even have crossed interstellar space in colonies. It could be a comfortable way to travel. They could then orbit the Sun and build new colonies to meet their requirements, until some of the new colonies moved on to explore other planetary systems.

I find it hard to imagine highly intelligent beings crossing the dark void of interstellar space themselves, however comfortable the transport facilities. My feeling is that such journeys are more likely to be made by intelligent robots if flights to other planetary systems are frequently made. The exception to this would be when civilizations are taking out insurance against future catastrophes. Super beings may be ready to make sacrifices to set up new societies to conserve their culture, but there would be no benefit for them in widespread colonization.

Life must Attract Life

Life-supporting planets are likely to be the most interesting places in the universe, and are always sure to attract interest. Consequently, the Solar System would have been a prime target for interstellar probes, and any monitoring system in place since the emergence of the human race might have brought more craft to a very rare event, knowing that the first successful technological species to evolve would rapidly change the planet. Developments during the past 10,000 years of human history might be far more interesting than, say, the 100 million years of dinosaur history, when any one million years would not have looked very different from the previous million years. Yet this interest in the inhabited worlds of other planetary systems should not extend to their take-over.

Although it may not be a rational decision for super-brained beings to begin to colonize all the worlds of the Galaxy, let us consider the time needed for such an enterprise. Our galaxy has more than 100 billion stars, and the colonizers would settle on planets or build space colonies from the debris which orbits stars. Sir Fred Hoyle and Professor Chandra Wickramasinghe, in their book 'Lifecloud" (1978), give two million years as the time needed for colonizing the Galaxy. They were focused on Earth-like planets suitable for colonization and assumed them to be 50 light-years apart. The top speed for the colonists was to be one-tenth the speed of light. This makes the average travel time to suitable planets 500 years. Hoyle and Wickramasinghe allow the colonists another 500 years for consolidation between each colonizing step. Therefore, as the diameter of the Galaxy is 100,000 light-years, it would take two million years to colonize it.

The assumed need for planets similar to the Earth for colonization has governed our past thinking on this subject. But a consideration of the biology involved, and the work of O'Neill, indicates that this was a big mistake. One can now see that Earth-like planets are not even desirable for so-called galactic colonization. Entering the biosphere of another world unprotected could be like exposing oneself simultaneously to all the plagues in history.

Consequently, habitable planets with flourishing biospheres may not figure in any colonization plans. We could, however, expect most planetary systems to have plenty of lifeless debris to use for building space colonies, so colonists could live secure from dangerous biological contamination – and there would be no need to cross 50 light-years to the nearest 'habitable planet'. Journeys of a few light-years, the average distance separating star systems, would be enough.

Eric M. Jones, who worked at the Los Alamos Laboratory, carried out a computer study of galactic colonization, building into his model various retarding factors, such as preliminary explorations of potential planetary systems by unmanned probes. (You can see here that Jones was thinking about finding Earth-like planets which, according to our scenario, would be prime targets to explore, but not to colonize.) Jones's colonizing ETs took their time, but still managed to colonize the Galaxy in only five million years, a small fraction of the time since the first technological life may have evolved. It could have taken a thousand times longer – there has been time enough.

The "gut feeling" of most scientists is that colonization or visits to the Solar System have not taken place. The reason they give is that there is no evidence of an alien presence. True, there is no *scientifically acceptable evidence*, but we have hardly begun to investigate the small proportion of UFO reports which might indicate the presence of extraterrestrial artefacts in our environment. They may not provide evidence, of course, but it is scientifically wrong to ignore a constant supply of reports from apparently credible sources, including the military, police and airline pilots, of vague phenomena which we cannot explain. Perhaps, therefore, we should maintain an open but rigorously scientific view of the best UFO data. The reason for thinking so is plain: the scientific rationale for ET's spacecraft being in the Solar System is the same as that needed to support the hypothesis that some ETs are broadcasting their messages to other worlds. If astronomical SETI is justified, so too is the scientific investigation of the UFO phenomena. But more of that in the next chapter.

The question we ask at this point is: do things look quieter out there than we would expect if space colonists were here? The answer may be negative if they were here to explore and study, rather than to colonize. We can accept that erosion would have soon wiped out any evidence of visits to the Earth, though evidence could exist on the erosion free Moon, or on Mars. Some scientists in the United States do claim that clear evidence of ET's activities exist on Mars, and that this will be confirmed by better close-up photography in the future. (See Chapter 11.) Yet evidence, if it exists, could be very difficult to discover, unless ET wanted us to do so, and we are not going to be able to say conclusively that there is no evidence within the Solar System until it is thoroughly explored. To date we have explored only about 99.9 per cent of the region in which ET could be present, so present we just cannot know what the situation is. The best we can do is to investigate any phenomena which may be relevant to SETI and try to form testable hypotheses. A "gut feeling" is not an adequate response, or a scientific one, to any question about the nature of life in the universe.

The Ultimate Eliminator

Frank Tipler, Professor of Mathematics and Physics at Tulane University, New Orleans, has been a brilliant critic of astronomical SETI, which he regards as a waste of time. His arguments, which depend on the development of self-reproducing robots (von Neumann machines), were widely publicised in the scientific press in the 1980s. His arguments are complex, but his message is simple. (See references to papers in Reference Section). Any ETs in this universe, he says, have had so much spare time since the first technological species evolved that they would have been here long ago, if they had existed. Therefore, as they are not seen walking the streets, or having a pint in the local pub, they do not exist.

The basic objection to this argument is that "absence of evidence is not evidence of absence". First, to be here, ETs would have had to cross interstellar space, perhaps "hopping" from planetary system to planetary system, if no better means of crossing the light-years exists. Since a thousand light-years or more might separate existing technological civilizations within the Galaxy, they may not have reached us yet. Thus any colonization of the Galaxy would depend on interstellar space flight being a routine activity for civilizations a few thousand years ahead of us. Even if such interstellar transport is available, an alien biosphere is not going to attract permanent ET residents who value their health. And if the ETs were inorganic robots, they might prefer their own custom-built colonies to the potential hazards of Earth. Finally, if anyone *has* visited Earth, they would presumably have wanted to study it, not destroy it, which might be the result if they became residents. Therefore, even if journeys from the stars are easy and hoards of ETs have entered the Solar System during the past few hundred million years, we wouldn't necessarily know anything about it.

The Trouble with Robots

However, Frank Tipler did introduce an awkward question into the subject by suggesting the possibility of von Neumann machines as the ultimate robots for the colonization of the Galaxy. There would be a potential danger in robots, whether they stayed on Earth or were launched into space – highly intelligent robots might make more robots. They could improve their species of robot with each generation, unlike mere biological beings who have reached their present state of development through millions of years of natural selection. It has taken a million years for our line in evolution to advance from Homo erectus to Homo sapiens. In theory, robots could take that step in one generation. A decade or two might be long enough. They would need to be more intelligent than Homo erectus to take that step, but our level of intelligence might be enough for a start. The robots could then proceed to produce superior robots to themselves. This way the dynasty of the robots could soon leave us behind. One cannot see where such a development might lead, but the advance and take over could be very rapid. Thus there would be a real potential danger for humanity if mobile robots ever reached our level of ability, with the freedom to make more robots.

The philosophical discussions about the future status of robots have failed to make the essential distinction between ourselves, as biological organisms, and robots which might possess a human level of awareness and intelligence. Some commentators maintain that if robots reach our level there would be no social distinction between us. There would have to be equality for robots, and that "racist" attitudes towards the robots would not be tolerated. What these good people, so deep in philosophical thought, have missed is the message from evolutionary biology. We are Darwinian machines. All progress (if we may call it that) is through natural selection. By contrast, all robots would be Lamarckian machines for which all improvements conceived or acquired by one generation could be incorporated into the next.

In 1801, half a century before Darwin's 'Origin of Species', the French biologist Jean Baptiste de Lamarck published his theory that animals evolved by passing on the characteristics acquired during their lives. The giraffe acquired its long neck, said Lamarck, because generations of giraffe stretched their necks skywards in order to reach more edible leaves. At the time, Lamarck provided a plausible explanation for the evolution of animals. However, half a century later,

Darwin provided a better explanation, while giving credit to Lamarck for developing the concept of evolution. The evolution of giraffes and all other life could be explained by natural selection. Those giraffes which had longer necks were able to reach leaves which those with shorter necks could not reach. Those with longer necks avoided starvation in hard times and survived to reproduce more offspring than shorter-necked giraffes. Consequently, generation after generation, giraffes gradually evolved longer necks until the optimum in neck-length was reached for the height of the trees where they lived.

Of course, necks can't evolve in isolation. There were other aspects of giraffe evolution and some mechanical limitations. Beyond a certain neck-length, any advantage would be outweighed by disadvantages. Giraffes have even had to evolve absorbent tissues in their necks, which control the flow of blood to the brain when they bend to drink. Evolution is a slow and complex process, whether the eventual product is a long neck or a large and intelligent brain.

Therefore, within a century or two, with the robots evolving according to Lamarck, humanity might be either replaced or put in a subservient position to the robots. Robots could take over the Earth and the Solar System, and perhaps head for the planetary systems of other stars. It follows that if you contribute to this process by launching your robots into interstellar space, you could aggravate the problem. With the ability to reproduce, your robots might advance to a level of power which could, within a few million years, put an end to all evolving biology in the Galaxy. This is the intimidating prospect of the so-called von Neumann machines, 'all purpose' robots which could roam through space, transforming everything in their path.

Here we come back to Frank Tipler's argument, so ably detailed in his four scientific papers. He maintains we are definitely alone in the Galaxy because the first world civilization to construct a von Neumann machine and send it on its way would conquer the Galaxy. (Actually the von Neumann machines, not their creators, would conquer the Galaxy, but we will put that point aside for the moment.) They would need to construct only one von Neumann machine which would be launched to the first star system, where it would find the materials and energy needed to make other von Neumann machines. These robotic offspring would then fly to other planetary systems and repeat the reproducing process. Within a few million years, every system would have at least one von Neumann machine in residence. While this colonization was in progress, the makers might benefit from a constant flow of information, as each planetary system was occupied. What Tipler's scenario describes is simply the possible result of Lamarckian machines being let loose on the Galaxy.

It was in 1948 that the great mathematician John von Neumann put forward this theory of self-reproducing machines or robots, which was later seized upon by people speculating about the colonization of the Galaxy. He simply called them 'self-reproducing automata' and said that they would need four components:

¤ An automated manufacturing facility.

¤ A set of instructions or program (a computer program).

¤ A means of executing the instructions.

¤ A controlling mechanism to decide which of the instructions are carried out at any given time.

What von Neumann was specifying are the mechanisms upon which all forms of life depend. Every living thing on this planet is a von Neumann machine, although no living organism can hand on any ability or attribute it acquires for itself to the next generation. (Bacteria are the exception to this. They can pass genes from one to another without natural selection. But that's another story.) Improvements, if we may call them that, come very slowly through the processes of organic evolution, through recombinations of genes and genetic mutations.

The most popular objection to the scenario of von Neumann machines conquering the Galaxy is that any civilization sufficiently advanced to make such robots would be a long-lived and stable society, probably with a high regard for its sense of responsibility. It would therefore not subject other civilizations to the danger of being taken over by alien machines. Moreover, a civilization that launched a von Neumann robot could also be in danger. Its more advanced descendants might return and take over the creators of its ancestor.

There is a dilemma here. From our limited view of the subject, intelligent probes, or robots as astronauts, appear to be the most practical way of crossing the light-years and exploring other worlds, if it is not done by astronomical SETI. The robots would need to have freedom to act, otherwise they could not explore other worlds for their masters back home. Yet the one thing they must not be allowed to do is to build improved versions of themselves. They cannot be let loose as Lamarckian machines, yet they would need to make more robots for work, if the exploration of other worlds is going to be pursued. This is the problem for the makers of bright robots: the robots can only be allowed to duplicate themselves with no improvements. How super societies will so limit their robots we have to leave to them. Maybe they will supply the robots with genes – make the robots into Darwinian machines similar to us. It's anybody's guess, but no one would want free-ranging von Neumann machines out in the Galaxy. The familiar science fiction nightmare of a computer taking over the world would be compounded a billion-fold by a computer taking over the Galaxy. No one would be able to stop the process.

Is there room for second thoughts? Well, artificial intelligence could be rational, while humans appear forever cursed with irrationality. Many years ago, when computers were called 'electronic brains' in the press, a distinguished biologist told me that he hoped computers would rapidly advance to a level at which they could take over government. He thought we would be better governed by rational computers than by irrational politicians. I wonder. At least we have some control over politicians, and they can't increase their powers by Lamarckian evolution!

The Colonization of Mars

All the discussions about the colonization of other planetary systems, by ETs or by us in the future, can be put into perspective by looking at what would be involved for us in the colonization of our next-door neighbour Mars. The problems we may face in colonizing Mars would be increased a million times in colonizing over interstellar distances.

Talk of turning Mars into a habitable planet has been naively optimistic. First, take the physical and chemical problems. Oxygen and nitrogen have to be released into the atmosphere (there's plenty of both elements locked up in sand and rocks). Mars today has an atmospheric pressure of 4.5 millimetres compared to 760 millimetres on the Earth. This means practically no atmosphere. The atmospheric pressure is so low that water boils on Mars at 0 degrees Centigrade, at the point at which it becomes solid on Earth. A substantial atmosphere would correct this inhospitable situation and increase the temperature. Water which has been frozen in the planet's crust for a few billion years would begin to flow on the surface, forming rivers and, perhaps, oceans of some sort. Water vapour in the developing atmosphere would raise the temperature further. But that's only the beginning: the establishment of the physical basis of a habitable planet.

Given that the colonists attain that stage, they then have to establish a stable ecosystem, one biosphere for the whole planet. We would have to carry the right sort of organisms to Mars. Balancing the right animals and plants, fungi and bacteria; having the right number of herbivores and carnivores throughout all the animal kingdom from insects to mammals; setting up food chains that will last. Noah had it easy by comparison with what would have to be done. Thousands of different species would be needed, yet gaps would soon show themselves in the food chains as ecosystem after ecosystem collapsed, necessitating rushed trips to Mars with appropriate organisms to fill the gaps. When flying to Mars is mere routine, like flying across the Atlantic, we may do this, but we, or rather our descendants, would need to possess a new level of space propulsion technology. There would be thousands of flights to Mars, a long procession of Noah's Arks heading out from Earth. The most difficult part of terraforming Mars may be after the atmosphere and water sources become stable, with temperatures at the right levels for the micro-organisms, including the photosynthesizing micro-organisms. These microbes run and maintain the oxygen, nitrogen and carbon dioxide cycles essential for life in our biosphere. Remove all the higher forms of life from Earth and life would go on. Remove all the bacteria, and all other life would die. It would be the same for Mars. Before higher life-forms (say, those which we can see) could be introduced, dynasties of bacteria would have had to be established and stabilised. They would then form the foundations for higher life.

We can see that to make Mars habitable for our own species would be a formidable job, taking at least hundreds of years if we had the space transport system to carry it through. The colonization of planets at interstellar distances, therefore, looks as near to an impossible task as anyone could imagine. Super civilizations may be able to do it, but it doesn't look a cost-effective exercise. My guess is that the colonization of other planetary systems would be for insurance purposes only. Exploration, yes. But colonization only where it is vitally necessary.

Chapter Eleven

Detection by Other Means

L et us indulge in some uninhibited speculation and try to think where evidence may have been left in the Solar System by interstellar probes, or travellers, during the past three to four billion years, or, more probably during the past 350 million years – since when the Earth's oxygen atmosphere would have been astronomically detectable by its spectral lines.

The Earth itself is the least likely place in which to find relics of ET, as erosion here so soon removes evidence of past events. On our time-scale for ET visitors, monuments like the great pyramids would soon disappear into the desert sands. Yet we need not travel far to find the best place in the Solar System for ancient evidence of visits, if such have ever been made. We need go only to the Moon which is so erosion free that the pyramids would last an eternity.

But if we are looking for immediate evidence, and are prepared to speculate that it is not impossible that ET may be within the Solar System in our time, then the most obvious phenomena to investigate are those described in the many unexplained UFO reports. These continue to increase in number with time. The question we have to ask is, therefore, can they all (many thousands of reports) be explained as natural physical events, misidentifications, the psychological condition of witnesses or hoaxes?

Most people (and that includes scientists) have gained their information about UFOs from the most publicised reports in the media, which have generally been of the sensational and unreliable kind. These stories attract the fantasy-prone who are soon having their own UFO experiences which, in turn, are reported by the media. So the mythology grows in size and power, smothering information that might be of scientific interest, and deterring rational people from approaching close enough to the subject to spot anything interesting.

Only Way Forward

We know from the experience of centuries that science offers the most reliable way to knowledge of life and the universe. Even though scientific "facts" are often approximations, they are the nearest to truth that we can reach at any given time. The scientific approach is, therefore, the best way to obtain results. If the UFO phenomena are ever to be explained, professional scientists will have to become involved. A few have become involved and testable hypotheses have been developed, but the science establishment shuns all such deviants. It's the same old story: go out on a scientific limb and the establishment will automatically try to cut it off. There is no funding for UFO research, and publication in the main science journals, for anyone who might try to have the results of their research published, is impossible. Of course, science journals have a right to demand an appropriate level in any research report they publish, and it must be admitted that few people who have studied the UFO phenomena have attained an appropriate level of scientific rigour.

The psychologists and sociologists, though, have not fared so badly. You can remain part of the science community and study the creations of fantasy-prone minds, and most scientists would put anyone who claimed to have boarded a flying saucer into that category. Parapsychology, which is often brought in to try and explain the UFO phenomena, just manages to survive as a subject for scientific research, but these two subjects, parapsychology and the ETH (extraterrestrial hypothesis), must be kept quite separate: a necessity which has not been accepted by many in the UFO societies which frequently deplore the neglect of the scientists. Parapsychology has no accepted scientific basis whereas the ETH of ufology has a great deal of indirect scientific support – just as much as supports astronomical SETI. It follows, therefore, that no aspect of the UFO phenomena can be scientifically explained in terms of parapsychology. That doesn't mean that parapsychology will not one day have scientific support, but it does mean that at present there is no scientifically acceptable evidence that our universe harbours phenomena which are parapsychological. We nevertheless have the absurdity of some people in UFO societies trying to explain something which we do not understand (the UFO phenomena) by referring to something else we do not understand (parapsychological phenomena). If we do wish to try and explain the UFO phenomena, it is obviously better to do so by reference to science that we do know and understand*.

Keeping the Blinkers on

Those scientists in astronomical SETI could provide the science, putting the most credible data of the UFO phenomena into perspective, but they haven't done so. A declared interest in UFOs could damage one's professional prospects, and most scientists would not spend the time needed to read into the subject. Scientists are used to referring to published scientific papers when they begin to investigate a new subject, and few scientific papers have been published on aspects of the UFO phenomena. The interesting scientific data, which comprises a tiny percentage of the whole, is mixed up with a mass of mythology and fantasy to deter most people who would be willing to explore the subject.

Newspaper journalists and broadcasters have not helped in this situation because hardly any of them are at all familiar with the relevant science. It's very rare to encounter a journalist (apart from the science journalists) who has even heard of astronomical SETI. Thus they are seldom equipped to point out what is ridiculous and what is scientifically interesting when reporting accounts of UFOs. To some extent this is excusable for journalists who have to cover every subject under the Sun, but many earnest investigators in the UFO societies, given a scientific approach and familiarity with the SETI rationale, could save themselves much time and trouble in pursuing false trails. Many writers have been too ready to accept accounts of flying saucers and visiting extraterrestrials without assessing the credibility of their data against the background science. These writers of books and articles have unintentionally done more than any critical scientist to discredit their subject.

ETs and UFOs

Interstellar exploration must be a well-established activity for it to be statistically possible for ET to be here in our time, monitoring the world from flying saucers. But for all we know it could be so. We

---

* See my book "The UFO Phenomena".

could speculate that details of the Earth have existed in extraterrestrial data banks for millennia, but that the ETs became far more interested in us only after we left the caves for city life. Human civilization has developed so rapidly compared to past developments on the planet that the past few thousand years would have been the best time to be here to monitor and record events. In prehistory each succeeding ten million years was much like the previous ten million years. If the time it has taken for our civilization to emerge since the origin of life is about average, new civilizations are going to be rare. News might, therefore, spread through the Immortal Network, the cosmic equivalent of the Internet, that a new technological species has evolved. The message would spread from planetary system to planetary system, "Come and take a look before it's too late!" Interest might grow in worlds near enough to pay us a visit. Even the simplest animal is of interest to some of us, so we might expect to be very interesting to the advanced minds of some ETs. They need only to be out there and have the necessary space technology to be in the Solar System at this time.

UFOs as Alien Artefacts

We therefore need to broaden SETI. If the scientific background is enough to justify searches for ET's broadcasts, then that same background is enough to support scientific searches for ET's space technology. The data on UFOs is often vague and dubious. It may all be mythology and misidentifications and psychology, even from credible sources such as the police, military and airline pilots. Nevertheless, a mass of data does exist. Astronomical SETI, by comparison, has no data to investigate, just a hypothesis to test which cannot be falsified – only confirmed. So the scientific neglect of the UFO phenomena is a strange attitude; especially as it is rather important to know if ET is a permanent guest or not. We may never have a normal conversation with any ET – try to imagine a conversation with a being a million years more advanced than yourself – but neither will our world be taken over. The ETs would not cross the light-years to acquire additional real-estate when it is hopelessly polluted by incompatible biological organisms, none of which could be trusted to provide a square meal without fatally disrupting an alien metabolism.

Permissible Probes

Many scientists in astronomical SETI have an attitude to the UFO phenomena which seems to prevent their entertaining the possibility that some UFO reports may indicate an ET presence. There is, of course, a conflict of interests: why watch for evidence of ET amongst the stars if he is already here watching us? Scientists who are active in astronomical SETI do accept the possibility that alien probes could have arrived in the Solar System, within, say, the past hundred million years. Given enough time, such a thing is possible, but they don't believe that probes could have arrived the day before yesterday when they could have arrived any time during the past few billion years. That is the problem scientists have with UFO reports, many of which seem to imply that the aliens arrived the day before yesterday. We have here the "time factor" problem. There have been a few billion years available for the first space technologists to explore the Galaxy and send their probes to the Solar System. So the more ancient the hypothetical probes are, the greater the possibility that they are here. Does that justify our brushing aside as nonsense all reports of craft in our environment which, according to the reports, could not possibly come from our own technology?

Let's keep the time factor in mind for a moment because it seems to have escaped the consideration of many scientists who are quite ready to state categorically that no extraterrestrial has ever visited the Solar System. Usually they say, "There's no evidence of extraterrestrial visitors in the Solar System." The point is that we are not yet in a position to know if there is any evidence or not. Neither would we expect to find evidence on Earth – it's the last place to find it, unless some of the reports of flying saucers do describe a physical reality in our environment.

This, of course, is exactly what many ufologists believe: that flying saucers are space probes which are monitoring the rapid development of our world civilization, although many ufologists seem unaware that a "time problem" exists. Since ET astronomers may have detected the spectral lines from our atmosphere during the past 350 million years, visits during that period are vastly more probable than visits during the past few thousand years. To change the statistical improbability of recent visits, the ETs must, in theory, have been coming here on a routine basis throughout prehistoric times. For the ETH of ufology to be correct, we must live on a well-studied and documented planet.

The fact that we have scientific reasons for thinking that we may not be the only technologists in the universe should make us cautious about instantly rejecting possible evidence of ET's artefacts in the Solar System, however nebulous that evidence may be. That something seems highly improbable should not stop us taking a look, when the implications of a positive finding are so great. Let's say that the ETH probably accounts for one in a hundred of the most credible reports of flying saucers; that's a low figure, but it's more than enough to justify professional research to test the hypothesis.

Odd Situation

It's rather odd that in the UFO literature the scientific base of astronomical SETI, which provides the best reason for taking some UFO reports seriously, has hardly ever been mentioned. It's as if the writers were unaware of its availability, and it's probably fair to say that many of them were and still are. This has led to an immense loss of credibility. The lack of a scientific approach has allowed writers on the UFO phenomena to accept many ridiculous reports and theories which are then perpetuated through the years by other writers. They have neglected what science has to offer, which has allowed much of the literature of ufology to expand into the realm of fantasy.

Speculation, based on what science we know, can enliven the mind and may be useful, but it has to be clearly defined as speculation. The problem with much UFO literature is that speculation is based on fantasy, which undermines the research and writings of the scientists and scientifically minded. Actually, if the UFO reports had to stand on their own, if the scientific rationale for SETI didn't exist, I would not be considering the UFO phenomena in this book. I would expect such phenomena as ball lightning, meteorological events, marsh gas and other local phenomena, plus the sociological-psychological causes, to explain all reports. The background science to SETI, however, gives a small proportion of reports a credibility, as far as the ETH is concerned, that they would not otherwise have. We can even say that some of the UFO reports provide the sort of evidence we might expect if ETs had discovered the Solar System and the fascinating activities on one of its planets.

One requirement for this speculation to be true is that interstellar space flight has to be a routine activity for a proportion of advanced civilizations, if only with automated spacecraft and robots of some kind. The second requirement is that the exploration of other planetary systems has to be something that advanced civilizations engage in over long periods of time (geological periods of time). We can see how this could be a future activity for us, something our civilization could be doing within a few centuries, given that a suitable propulsion system for spacecraft can be found. At present we don't have that propulsion system, and the space age cannot really take off until we do.

Part of the second requirement, which may be psychologically more difficult to accept, is that the flying saucer phenomenon must have existed for a very long time – perhaps for millions of years. This is necessary to make the hypothesis statistically feasible. Obviously, the more world civilizations that engage in interstellar space flight and planetary exploration, the less important this requirement becomes, but it's still a basic requirement for the ETH. If the Earth has been open to visits for a few billion years, and has been astronomically detectable as a blue planet for at least 350 million years (detectable by the spectral lines of ozone and oxygen), it is not statistically probable that our neighbourly extraterrestrial s have only just decided to call.

We can speculate that for its first 3.5 billion years the Earth remained undetected. Anyway, the life on our planet during that time would have interested only the alien equivalent of microbiologists. Nothing else but bacteria flourished until about 1.5 billion years ago when advanced single-celled organisms evolved. Only at the beginning of the Cambrian Period (570-500 million years ago) did life display the lifeforms, at a basic level, that we know today. The rate of evolution has been almost exponential since then, so that the Earth has become a far more interesting place with the passage of time. We can speculate further (in complete absence of any supporting evidence) that the number of technological civilizations has increased with the passage of time, so that blue planets like the Earth, once discovered, would attract an increasing amount of attention from the advanced inhabitants of other blue planets.

Lunar Astro-Archaeology

There is obviously the possibility that, during the past few billion years, alien probes or space colonies have entered the Solar System and deposited evidence. The great star fields orbit the galactic centre so that a few million Sun-like stars have passed within several light-years of the Solar System since its formation. And where would be the best place to leave evidence for future space travellers from Earth? The Moon looks like the best place, being free from erosion and the nearest world to us, but where on the Moon might evidence be found? ETs capable of bridging the light-years are unlikely to be ambiguous, if they wanted to leave a message. Perhaps the centres of very large impact craters (some of which possess prominent central peaks) could be the kind of places to look. The largest lunar craters have existed for more than three billion years; that is, since the last great meteorites were swept up by the planets and their moons. Tycho is 54 miles in diameter with the main display of rays on the Moon. The rays show where streams of matter fell, having been ejected into space and thrown across the Moon's surface by the explosive impact of a large meteorite. Copernicus, with its prominent rays, is a hundred miles across. The early bombardment within the Solar System made larger craters on the Moon, but these filled with lava some four billion years ago, forming what we know as the *marias* or lunar seas, vast plains surrounded by old crater walls. At present there are no indications that ET has left his calling card on the Moon, but as this bleak, erosion-free world is explored, someone some day may stumble upon evidence of previous visitors, though many millions of years might separate their footsteps on the Moon from ours.

Biological Messages

Carl Sagan* once suggested that 'perhaps the messages are already here, present in some everyday experience that we have not made the right mental effort to realize'.

Two Japanese biologists in Tokyo, Hiromitzu Yokoo of Kyorin University Hachioji, and Tairo Oshima of the Mitsubishikasei Institute of Life Sciences, later searched for such a message in the basis of life itself. They speculated that a simple organism, a bacterium, might carry a message in its DNA molecules. As DNA and RNA (nucleic acids) initiate the manufacture of life's every protein, and thus code for every attribute of every species of life on Earth, the Japanese biologists thought that a communicative ET might have placed a message in this most advanced of all coding systems. How ET could do this, when an organism's DNA has to specify a viable

---

* In 'Cosmic Connection', Hodder and Stoughton, 1973.

organism for life in a particular environment on Earth, is not at all clear.

Anyway, Yokoo and Oshima tested their hypothesis that a bacteriophage known as ΦX174 held an ET message. A bacteriophage (usually called a phage) is a micro-organism that infects bacteria. As Yokoo and Oshima said, "Phage ΦX174 is a virus infection to an enteric bacterium inhabiting the colon of the only intelligent beings on Earth." In short, it attacks a bacterium in the human gut. The bacterium is *Escherichia coli*, an organism widely used in molecular biology. The phage which attacks E. coli is, therefore, very simple and has a comparatively simple genetic message. Yokoo and Oshima also chose phage ΦX174 because its DNA sequence was the first to be determined

They studied a prominent section of the DNA (a section of overlapping genes) for a message, interpreting it in various ways, but concluded that it contained no ET message. However, the idea that it might contain a message does seem about as improbable as anything could be. I can't help asking myself if ET would put a message in an organism that is entirely dependent on a second organism for its continued existence? Or send a message across interstellar space that went straight to the bowels of the recipient rather than to his brain?

As Yokoo and Oshima acknowledged, "There are hundreds of small phages infectious to E. coli, ΦX174 is one of them and the question is which virus, if any, carried an extraterrestrial message." The fact to be faced is that the number of different phages and other microbes is vast. In theory, one of them might carry an ET message in its DNA molecules, although in reality this possibility is too remote for serious consideration. One could almost suspect that the report by Yokoo and Oshima was a hoax on the readers of SETI research papers.

Even if we allow that an organism on Earth might carry an ET message, then surely it would be an independent organism with something to indicate its importance as a message carrier. After all, we cannot see an organism's DNA and can hardly make detailed analyses of every species on Earth to see if one just happens to carry a celestial message. There are far more organisms to investigate than there would be target stars in any SETI project. Therefore, can we spot any organism that might have its genetic origins in the stars? Maybe the time has come for naturalists, as well as astronomers, to look for ET messages, but I don't think so.

Ezekiel's Spaceships

Earlier we considered the statistical improbability of ET visits in historical times – during the past 4 thousand years rather than at other times during the past 4,000,000,000 years. Such visits seem improbable unless ETs have been coming here for millions of years and the Earth is a well-studied and recorded planet. We can accept that the Sun could have supported ET space colonies throughout the past 4,000,000,000 years, perhaps in or near the asteroid belt where plenty of building materials exist. And ETs could, in theory, have established themselves in planetary systems near to us. Such a presence within the Solar System or orbiting the nearest stars would be beyond our powers to detect, but would make visiting ETs during historical times more feasible. Most books published on historical astronauts have not withstood examination by anyone who understands the relevant historical and scientific background, yet the possibility of ET visits cannot be dismissed. There are a few reported visits – just a few – that offer information that we can seriously assess and I will relate two of them.

Josef Blumrich was Chief of the Systems Layout Branch at NASA's Marshall Space Flight Center, working on the Saturn Rocket and the design of Skylab, when, by chance, he came upon the suggestion that the Old Testament prophet Ezekiel had described the visits of spaceships more than 2,500 years ago. Blumrich investigated the suggestion, expecting to show it groundless, but instead found himself discovering a description of a 2,500 year-old spaceship, well-designed for Earth exploration. Later he wrote a book about his investigations*.

Being a religious man, Ezekiel thought he was being visited by God, or his emissaries. To most men the arrival of a spaceship, or God, a few hundred yards away would inhibit detailed observation, yet Ezekiel, obviously someone of high intelligence and strong character, described his encounters with precision. In Chapter 1, verse 4, he refers to the encounter which Blumrich interprets as a spaceship landing:

"And I looked, and, behold, a whirlwind came out of the north, a great cloud, and a fire unfolding itself, and a brightness was about it

---

* "The Spaceships of Ezekiel", Corgi, 1974. Also Blumrich's later account in Unesco's science quarterly "Impact" (the second edition of 1975.)

and out of the midst thereof as the colour of amber, out of the midst of the fire."

Blumrich wrote, "We should consider that Ezekiel first saw this vehicle at a distance of about 1,000 metres; at that moment the nuclear engine fired, probably with some white clouds of condensation." To Ezekiel this was God's fiery chariot descending like thunder through the clouds. Blumrich, who used six different biblical translations, wrote that by the time he reached verse 7 of Chapter 1 he was already interpreting the prophet's words as spaceship landing legs. "Their legs were straight, and the soles of their feet were round: and they sparkled like burnished bronze," wrote Ezekiel. The rounded 'soles of their feet' was the very design used by Blumrich and his colleagues at NASA to allow the legs of a space vehicle to slide on landing.

The "legs" belonged to what Ezekiel described as four "living creatures with wings", but their wings were obviously not birdlike in their form and function, judging by Ezekiel's descriptions, and Blumrich sees them as the blades of the spacecraft's four helicopter landing units. From each of the four landing units a wheel was then deployed. The wheels, the only objects familiar to Ezekial, were different from any wheels he had known, and he described them in detail. "Yet no one," wrote Blumrich, "has ever taken seriously the functional description which indicates that the wheels could move in any direction without being turned or steered." Blumrich certainly took the description seriously and went on to design the Omnidirectional Wheel, for which he obtained a patent in 1974. Blumrich thought that it could improve the mobility of invalid wheelchairs, an appropriate spin-off from biblical space technology.

The spacecraft's shape, reconstructed by Blumrich, is that of a humming top, a shape well suited to accommodate the four helicopter landing units and for entry into the Earth's atmosphere. A similar design was, in fact, tested at NASA's Langley Research Center in the late 1960s. Blumrich analysed a range of weights, sizes, shapes and power factors for Ezekiel's spaceship, and was left in no doubt of the craft's feasibility. "The only component we could not build," wrote Blumrich, "is the nuclear engine which could take several decades to develop."

The question, of course, is whether this spaceship really belongs to Ezekiel or to Blumrich? It seems highly unlikely that a visiting spaceship could be so close to us in its technology. We should expect the technology of any ET neighbour to be separated from us by millions of years rather than thousands. Yet, according to Blumrich, the spaceship Ezekiel described 2,500 years ago was scarcely more advanced than we could build today. The technological ceiling for spaceships would have to be very low in order to make this probable. Ezekiel gives no indication in his long account of the visitors that they had any other than human form. He had four contacts with them during 20 years. Only the commander and the messenger have a space age quality: they wore suits of burnished gold which Blumrich interprets as spacesuits. Did Ezekiel simply describe a vision which, by coincidence, an imaginative space engineer, 2,500 years later, interpreted as a visiting spaceship?

The Nommos from Sirius

My next account is of an event which occurred 3,000 years before Ezekiel (3,500 BC), when, it is claimed, creatures from the Sirius star system visited Earth. There was no confusing these visitors with humans, as the Ezekiel case seems to do. These ETs were amphibious. The case was studied and described by Robert Temple, an American scholar who set out the historical and anthropological data in a book*.

Temple's thesis starts with the Dogons, a race still living in West Africa. Several years before he wrote his book, Temple's interest was captured by the findings of two French anthropologists, Germaine Dieterlen and Marcel Griaule, who had studied the Dogons between 1946 and 1950. The mythology of the Dogons, Temple thought, contained unexpected scientific knowledge. It also contained a description of a landing of amphibious beings, the Nommos, and Temple began to wonder if the Dogons might have gained their knowledge from this extraterrestrial source.

The mythology of the Dogons tells how the Nommos spacecraft landed, and then moved to a hollow which filled with water, enabling the amphibious astronauts to disembark in watery comfort. Later they splashed about there in their leisure hours, after hard days teaching primitive man the arts of civilization. Although the Dogons revere the Nommos, they describe them as an 'abomination' and repulsive which, as Temple pointed out, is not the normal description of ancient gods. But what information did the Nommos provide, if any?

---

* "The Sirius Mystery", Sidgwick and Jackson, 1976.

Mainly it was about the Sirius system of stars, so important in Dogon mythology. The Dogons knew that Sirius A, the brightest star in the sky (intrinsically 26 times brighter than the Sun), has an unseen companion, Sirius B. They say, "It is the heaviest star." Indeed, it is very heavy, being a white dwarf – a collapsed star weighing about 2,000 tons per cubic foot.

The Dogons knew that Sirius B takes 50 years to orbit Sirius A. They also had other astronomical information. However, the only information new to us, which they claim to have received from the Nommos, is that the Sirius system has a third star with a planet. This star, say the Dogons, is larger than Sirius B. After Temple published his findings, astronomers searched for the star. No one has found it.

One would expect Sirius A, the most brilliant star in the sky, to gather a few myths in the course of history. Western missionaries, and other non-extraterrestrials visiting the Dogons, would have talked about it, so providing the Dogons with their astronomical information, which they simply incorporated into their mythology. We know from New Guinea how events and new knowledge from World War 2 were quickly turned into the mythologies of giant flying birds which brought presents of food. The Dogons had more oppor-tunity to develop myths, through their earlier contact with Western-ers, than the people of New Guinea.

The heaviness of Sirius B, the very first white dwarf discovered, was known about more than 50 years ago, whilst its existence was determined between 1830 and 1840 by the German astronomer Friedrich Bessel from the wavy path of Sirius A across the heavens (in the same way that, in recent times, some astronomers have attempted to detect evidence of planets orbiting nearby stars). The star was first seen by Alvan Clark in 1862.

Temple claims that the information which the Dogons possess is really more than 5,000 years old and was possessed by the ancient Egyptians in pre-dynastic times, before 3,200 BC. He adds that the Dogons are, in part, descended culturally from the ancient Egyptians. This dating of the Dogon information is crucial to Temple's thesis and unproved. We know that the peoples of the ancient world had great knowledge and understanding, which was lost and then partly rediscovered in Europe at the dawn of modern science. But was all of it rediscovered by the methods of science? Temple claims that Kepler, a devoted reader of the Greek philosopher Proclus, may not have been as original in his achievements as we suppose. However, there's no reason to suppose that any knowledge in the ancient world was gained from extraterrestrial visitors.

Another objection to Temple's thesis is that the Sirius star system is not a likely home for life, unless the Nommos were colonizers of that system and living in O'Neill-type habitats – suitably amphibious ones, we must suppose. According to current astrophysical theory, if planets could evolve in binary and multiple star systems, such as the Sirius system, they would offer unstable conditions for life, unless the component stars were widely separated, or very close. In any case, Sirius A is a very young star: only about 500 million years old. This star will end its life-cycle long before advanced life could evolve on any planet in the Sirius system.

The whole Sirius system cannot be older than Sirius A. The Solar System, by comparison, is ten times older and life has been evolving on Earth for a period seven times greater than the age of Sirius A. Not much time, therefore, for the Nommos to have evolved. Moreover, Sirius B, at one time a more massive and brighter star than Sirius A (and, therefore, a shorter-lived star), must have exploded or become very unstable in the process of becoming a white dwarf.

So what about the Nommos stories? Like all such stories we need information unknown to us, predictions that we can check. The more unexpected they are, the better. An example of what I mean is found in the accounts of the Phoenicians who travelled around Africa 3,000 years ago. Their claim that they sailed around Africa might well be doubted today had the Phoenicians not also reported that they observed the stars travelling in the wrong direction. At the time, such a reported observation might have caused them to be disbelieved, but for us it confirms their story because, of course, this is what they would have seen when travelling from the northern into the southern hemisphere.

Temple's thesis (though a scholarly study of historical and anthropological material) seems only slightly more substantial than the many reports of flying saucers whose occupants leave Earth with no more than a few casual words to the residents. We might expect that creatures capable of interstellar space flight would leave behind more than the Dogons have incorporated in their mythology. The Dogons did provide just one piece of information that we did not already know: that in the Sirius system there is a third star, four times the size of Sirius B. Any excitement that Temple's thesis initially caused evaporated after astronomers failed to find it – they would certainly have done so if it had existed.

Visits in our Time?

Let us now look at conceivable visits in our time, at what has become known as the extraterrestrial hypothesis (the ETH) of the UFO phenomena*. There are thousands of reports of UFOs, and some are not inconsistent with what we could expect if we were being monitored and studied by other worlds. The problem is that only a small proportion of UFO reports stand up to close examination. There exists a powerful mythology at work which causes many people to report unusual visual experiences as UFOs, which they are, although not from another world. Nevertheless, there are many cases which cannot be explained after exhaustive investigations.

Many reports in the extensive UFO literature are obvious hoaxes, illusions or cases of mistaken identity. It is, nevertheless, a possibility that ET colonies could be in the asteroid belt or further out, living on energy from the Sun, without our knowing about it. We may instinctively feel that this is such a remote possibility that it does not deserve serious consideration, but this is only a gut reaction. We cannot show that ET is *not* out there, and there have been numerous inexplicable events which might indicate that he is. However, there are hypotheses, put together by a few "reckless" scientists, which could be tested. This line of research could show the importance, or otherwise, of the UFO phenomena in SETI, but financial backing for such research is almost impossible to obtain when associated with UFOs, even though its scientific rationale is the same as that supporting astronomical SETI.

Some UFOs, such as the persistent Hessdalen UFOs (oddly behaving lights in Central Norway), may eventually be explained in terms of physics, the mechanism of which, though currently unknown to us, may be discovered. But what lies behind the "nuts-and-bolts" flying saucers, which have been photographed and recorded on video tapes by apparently credible people in many parts of the world?

The triangular UFOs observed and reported by the United States Air Force at a top-security base (Rendlesham in Britain), by the police and air force in the Belgium Wave of UFOs of 1993-94, and in many other parts of the world are described with an intriguing consistency of detail. The status of so many of the witnesses has been such that one would not expect them all to be affected by the mythology of

---

* See "The UFO Phenomena" by Edward Ashpole.

UFOs, which is undoubtedly the basis of a high proportion of reports. Then there are the strange luminous phenomena which frequent our atmosphere, sometimes near ground level and sometimes at altitudes of about 30,000 feet and higher, where they surprise airline crews whose companies tell them, quite reasonably, to say nothing of their observations. There are unexplained cases where entire crews of airliners have witnessed UFOs. Perhaps the airline companies should ask the atmospheric physicists to look for answers. None of the numerous atmospheric physicists I've talked with has a hypothesis to offer, or has been asked to carry out any investigations.

We can never know what lies behind these strange phenomena if we do not take steps to investigate. The scientific and technological viewpoint which SETI has given us during the past few decades suggests (let's put it no stronger) that at least some of the UFO phenomena provide the sort of vague and inexplicable evidence we might expect from a very advanced technology, the scientific basis of which we would not understand.

How close we are to the technology of visiting spacecraft, if that is what some UFOs are, would depend on the height of the ceiling to technologically applicable knowledge. Judging by the characteristic space flight of some UFOs (as reported and recorded on video tape), they might be based on a complete understanding of fundamental physics. In other words, the makers of those craft could have reached the ceiling in this particular area of knowledge. We could therefore only hope to duplicate saucer technology, in time, if there exists in this universe a low ceiling to science and technology – one that Homo sapiens might reach. If such an attainable ceiling exists, then all successful technological civilizations could rise to that ceiling. At that final stage they would have basically similar technologies dependent on the same understanding of nature. If that ceiling is only a century or two away from our advancing science and technology, then those few optimistic scientists who hope to understand how saucers work may not be hopelessly distant from the reality of the situation. Otherwise, the speculations about UFO flight will take us nowhere.

One interesting point is that the flight characteristics of UFOs seem to defy gravity. This is interesting because particle physicists will tell you that the major question in physics today is the nature of mass. What gives matter the quality of mass? It we knew what produces mass at the sub-nuclear level, we might just conceivably find a way of removing it from objects, or nearly so. This might provide the propulsion system we need to enter the real Space Age because we are never going to go far in space if we have to rely on chemical rockets. Nearly massless spacecraft would need a minimal amount of fuel and could defy gravity in all the ways reported by the thousands of witnesses of flying saucers. So will we one day be able to use gravity instead of continuously fighting against it?*

Ghosts and Ghouls

Most scientists obtain their information on UFOs from the popular media. No surprise, therefore, that they go along with the journalists and categorise UFOs along with ghosts and ghouls and things that go bump in the night. Most scientists are so highly specialised these days that they are not aware of all the data, brought together by those in astronomical SETI, which provides a rationale for the ETH of ufology, and sharply separates UFO phenomena from anything in the paranormal camp. The only group of scientists who are aware, at least subconsciously, of this backing from science are those in astronomical SETI, and they have personal and professional reasons for not looking. Who is going to provide millions of dollars to search for ET's broadcasts from the stars, if ET is already here, flying around the world in saucers?

Thus the UFO phenomena will not go away, and we don't know what the truth is. Only a few people have used the available science and technology in a continuous and methodical way to try and find answers. Reports of landings, for example, have never been properly investigated. There have been several thousand landings reported in all parts of the world, yet evidence that might have existed at the time has hardly ever been searched for scientifically. Anyone who cares to read the UFO literature can verify this for themselves.

More than anything else, the published investigations of UFO landings are mostly a study in how not to study such landings. Investigators of landing sites are (with rare exceptions) not research scientists. They therefore cannot be expected to provide the level of scientific rigour and technical know-how needed. Enthusiasm and hard work are not enough. What is needed is a research programme with specialist teams, each consisting of a physicist, analytical chemist, microbiologist and molecular biologist. Funding for such a pro-

---

*I have dealt with this subject in detail in "The UFO Phenomena".

gramme would be very modest because the teams would probably be called out only once or twice a year, but they would have to be ready to go and examine sites at short notice. To call out a local scientist, who may be unfamiliar with the UFO phenomena and not able to give much time to an investigation, is not the way to study reported landings. The probability of discovering anything interesting may not be high, but the chance of coming to scientific grips with the phenomena is enough to warrant modest support for research, so that the most credible reports of landings could be investigated as soon as they were received.

The most comprehensive research so far of a UFO landing was carried out by scientists working for SEPRA, a group within the French space agency (the Centre National d'Etudes Spatiales). A small UFO landed in the garden of a Monsieur Renato Nicolai in Trans-en-Provence at about five o'clock on the 8th of January, 1981. Within days the landing site and the surrounding area had been investigated by the police and scientists working for SEPRA. Specialists at French Universities analysed the samples taken and Professor Michel Bounias, of the National Institute of Agronomy Research in Avignon, carried out a detailed study of the effects of the landing on surrounding vegetation. The final report concluded that "something" had landed, leaving definite and measurable effects. Obviously, what that "something" was no one in SEPRA could say, but the importance of the Trans-en-Provence investigation (and other investigations by scientists working for SEPRA) is that it shows what can and should be done with reported landing sites, when such reports can be accepted as credible*

Many reports of landings, of course, do not warrant an investigation. What makes one suspicious of UFOs as a source of extraterrestrial contact is the rich variety of 'visitors' reported. Saucernauts have apparently come from all parts of the Solar System: from Venus, Mars and Jupiter. More reasonably, they also come from other planetary systems of stars we know and stars we don't know, even from other galaxies. What is more, they have all arrived in our lifetime to see us.

In some reports, the saucernauts who actually land make a hasty retreat to their saucers on the approach of witnesses, or, when they do give interviews, they are too inclined to moralize to ring true. They have come, claim the reports, to tell us the error of our ways and how

---

*To find out more about the Trans-en-Provence case and the work of SEPRA see *Appendix 1: References and Recommended Books.*

to save the world. They have crossed interstellar space, yet tell us nothing we do not already know or could easily make up. Their messages, as reported in newspapers and magazines, could be written by any crank and probably are. But these cranky UFO reports help to sell newspapers and magazines. They also provide entertaining stories which do not have to be checked. No newspaper editor has to worry about the truth or otherwise of UFO reports. Readers lap them up, credible or not, so put them in. Never let the facts interfere with a good story.

Should we expect Evidence?

Most people with a scientific turn of mind say that if UFOs were extraterrestrial , then some evidence of this would have been discovered by now. But is this fair comment?

Arthur C. Clarke once wrote that it would be easier to hide a dinosaur in Manhattan than to conceal a visit by an extraterrestrial spaceship. In a television programme on the truth about flying saucers and their occupants, Clarke maintained that any arrival here of an extraterrestrial intelligence would be unmistakable for what it was. Such a visit would enter our lives in a spectacular fashion, and we would know all about it. There would be no element of doubt, as there is today about the nature of flying saucers.

I can't help but come to the opposite conclusion. Put yourself in a spaceship in Earth orbit and travel back a million years – it's a very versatile spaceship. You are then in a good position to study our early and direct ancestor Homo erectus. You send down a craft to investigate and you find them, living in small groups, mostly on the African savannahs. Now you wouldn't land your craft among them, jump out and say, "Hello, there! I've just come from the future to study your primitive society and to help you move out of those uncomfortable caves into a more satisfying way of life." Such action would be worse than inappropriate if you wanted to learn anything about the ways of Homo erectus. You would only cause panic, and probably destroy any opportunity of valuable research.

What, then, would you do if you were not a Homo sapiens visiting his ancestors but an ET visiting Earth sometime after the first Homo sapiens evolved? You have on board your flying saucer all the technology you need for your study of human society. I think that you would observe from a distance, trying at all costs to avoid making your presence known. The next move might be to capture a few individuals for closer study, taking them to your custom-built space colony which orbits the Sun and has all the necessary life-supporting technology on board. You might then, in time, persuade your captives or their offspring to act as co-operative assistants. This way you might eventually get to know and understand the society of Homo sapiens, but you wouldn't have plans to take over or live in their society. The closest you would come to this would involve getting to know a few individuals as well as you could, while studying human society from the outside, as we study any monkey or ape society in the wild today.

Judging from the UFO reports, this is exactly what the occupants of flying saucers are doing – that is, if they exist to do anything. Let's assume they have avoided close contact with our society while studying us at a distance. When you think about it, the old science fiction cliché, "Take me to your leader," is the last thing any visiting extraterrestrial s with the appropriate linguistic skill would say. They would know enough about us when they landed to be able to go straight to "our leader" unaided, if they so wished.

I know this "contact avoidance" scenario is contradicted by the close contact and abduction stories, but are any of these stories credible? There are thousands of them yet not one item of information from an extraterrestrial source that we could test. We need some information that is as yet unknown to us, but which could be confirmed by us. Neither is there an item of ET's technology or biology, or an interesting scrap of anything we could analyse. Another objection to the stories from those who claim to have had conversations with the occupants of flying saucers, is that they seem to think it perfectly acceptable that ETs have arrived for the first time last weekend, which, of course, is unacceptable. Almost everything that has been published about UFOs and visitors to Earth has neglected the "time problem". If ET is here now, there must have been, for statistical reasons, a whole series of visits dating back at least a few hundred million years.

And so we come back to the exploration hypothesis (not the colonization hypothesis of Frank Tipler and his supporters). The essential point is that it is a testable hypothesis that awaits a proper testing. Perhaps the best-developed theory is that of Roy Dutton, an engineer who worked for most of his professional life for British Aerospace. He worked on the problems posed by the many reports of the flight characteristics of UFOs, and eventually concluded that their arrivals and departures must be governed by specific orbits and orbital periods of the Earth. With the use of computers, he developed an elaborate system of orbits and entry points from space which accounted for the precise times and places provided in hundreds of UFO reports. It took Dutton more than 25 years of spare-time research to develop his theory, the Astronautical Theory. It can now be tested astronomically by searching on specific coordinates for space vehicles in retro-orbits with a 65.4 minute orbital period. A vehicle in retro-orbit is travelling in the opposite direction to the Earth's rotation, and a considerable amount of energy has to be available to maintain a vehicle in such an orbit. A few amateur astronomers are beginning to test Dutton's theory*.

Any old Artefacts

The evidence which Frank Tipler believes does not exist, does not have to consist of impressive monuments to a higher culture or noticeable space probes and colonies orbiting in the Solar System. There could be alien waste material orbiting somewhere of the kind which we have managed to accumulate in Earth orbit, such as dumped equipment. The Moon, which is erosion free, and Mars, which is nearly so, are good candidates for future alien artefact hunters. If anyone has explored these worlds during the past few hundred million years they may have left enough evidence of their visits for present detection. There would have been no need for them to have constructed a monument to mark the spot! No one can say there is no evidence of ET within the Solar System until the surfaces of the Moon and Mars have been thoroughly explored.

A story told by Ben Finney, an anthropologist at the University of Hawaii, at the SETI Conference in Val Cenis, France in 1990, revealed that NASA itself entertained thoughts of finding evidence of ET on Mars. "One of the archaeologists in my department," said Finney, "likes to tell the story about how, one day in the mid-1960s, when he was a doctoral student at the University of Arizona, he was approached by his professor, who asked if he would be interested in applying to be a scientist astronaut. It seems that NASA had contacted the professor and told him that they might want an archaeologist to

---

* Roy Dutton's research and his theory require far more space to explain than I have available in this book, but there is a chapter on this work in "The UFO Phenomena". For contact address, see *Appendix 1: References and Recommended Books*.

go to Mars to investigate the possibility that intelligent, artefact-pro-
ducing life, might once have existed there."

Are we there yet?

We have obviously made great progress in SETI because we have
testable hypotheses. This has moved the subject into science. Nevertheless, sometimes I wonder if we may still be as far from contact
with extraterrestrial intelligence as were those late-nineteenth and
early-twentieth-century scientists who wanted to communicate with
the Martians by lighting massive fires and by constructing giant
right-angle triangles on the sands of the Sahara to show that at least
we understood geometry. For example, when Mars was at its closest
approach to Earth in 1941, Sir James Jeans suggested that searchlights
might be used to flash the prime numbers (3,5,7,11,13,17 and so on)
to any mathematically minded Martians. Of course, in 1941 there
were plenty of searchlights in wartime Britain, although no Martians
to see them.

These old suggestions, which appear hopelessly naïve today, were
put forward by sensible and clever people – sometimes by leading
scientists of their time. Intelligent Martians were a possibility from
what we knew about Mars in 1941. Such old ideas, I think, should
make us both cautious and modest in what we propose, yet not too
inhibited. Boldness may pay off one day. Whatever the outcome of
the search for evidence of ETs, the thinking that must precede the
search must open our minds a little. Though simple in conception
and following logically from the Copernican revolution, the hypothesis of the plurality of inhabited worlds, for which brave Bruno was
burnt to death in 1600, is, nevertheless, the grandest idea to come out
of science. No other scientific hypothesis can have more profound
implications for human thought, whatever the results from testing it.

Human Limitations

We have to ask if we are capable of understanding every phenomena
which we may encounter? Every intelligent species we observe shows
its limitations in awareness and understanding, and there seems no
reason why we should think our species an exception. The idea that
this brain of ours, which has evolved through a rather coincidental
set of circumstances, is the key to understanding everything the

universe has to offer cannot be correct. This may be hard to accept. Science has given us so much knowledge that our capacity to understand begins to look unlimited. We live in such a golden age of new knowledge and ideas about nature that many scientists do believe that the human brain is without limitations!

Yet this seems unlikely. We may never gain complete understanding of the universe, of how it came into being and what lies at the heart of its reality. It does seem strange, therefore, that we should search with such vigour to answer questions about the fundamental nature of the universe while we neglect the great question about the status of life in the universe. In theory we could confirm that life and intelligence are universal phenomena and part of the great scheme of things. In theory we may never understand the fundamental nature of the universe and how it came into being.

The Most Probable Scenario

What then is the most probable scenario that we may have to cope with? We are guessing, of course, and the scientific evidence in many areas is too vague for even tentative conclusions, but we have to guess to provide hypotheses for scientific attention.

The scenario is that technological civilizations discover the scientific basis for interstellar space flight within a thousand years or so from where we are today, given that such a scientific basis exists to be discovered. If it doesn't then no one is going to travel from planetary system to planetary system, and even small interstellar probes, depending on our currently envisaged methods of space propulsion, may not provide a routine way of exploring neighbouring stars and their planets.

However, if interstellar travel is easy for civilizations which are merely thousands of years ahead of us technologically (a brief moment on the cosmic time-scale), then we could reasonably expect evidence to exist that the Earth is being monitored because, for statistical reasons, we should be the most recent technological civilization to have evolved – and a rare event. Advanced beings are not going to miss such a spectacle if they can send probes to observe what is going on. We would do the same in their position.

Three things would get in the way of this scenario being roughly correct:

1.   We are the only technological species in the Galaxy in our era.

2. There are other world civilizations, but they are too distant and have not yet had time to reach us.

3. The scientific basis for the appropriate level of interstellar space flight does not exist and journeys to the stars are hardly ever made because of the enormous difficulties.

If statements two and three are correct (and statement one incorrect), the radio astronomers in SETI are on the right track and good luck to them, because our only contact with ETs can be by broadcasting, providing our astronomers can tune into to the right frequency at the right time. If none of those three statements is correct, then the few per cent of credible UFO reports may be our only indication that our scenario of the situation out there is roughly correct.

One per cent is Enough

Let's be cautious and say that just one per cent of the data published in ufology is worth serious consideration. Most scientists know nothing of that one per cent and wouldn't want to wade through the other 99 per cent to find it. Yet that one per cent might – just might – provide a key to a revelation about our position in the world in relation to other life in the universe. It would not be easy for scientists to begin to investigate the UFO phenomena, even if they wanted to: their professional reputations would be in jeopardy if it became known that they were meddling in things ufological. Hardly any full-time scientific research has been carried out with official blessing and financial support. One prominent exception was the famous Condon investigation and report in the United States, which cost half-a-million dollars, but was more like a judicial enquiry than a scientific investigation.

Monuments of Mars?

If the Solar System has been explored, especially during the past 350 million years since oxygen and ozone have been signalling the presence of a flourishing biosphere on this planet, then future astronauts may find evidence on the Moon and Mars where extraterrestrial relics might have survived for millions of years. Obviously, in our present state of ignorance, we can't put a figure on our chances of finding evidence of ET's visits to the Moon and Mars and this also applies to any possible evidence elsewhere within the Solar System. Yet the scientific case for SETI is strong enough for us not to neglect sources of possible evidence. It's rather ironic, therefore, that scientists in astronomical SETI, whose research arm is radio astronomy, who have established a powerful case for the probable presence of ET out there, are amongst those who tend to reject the possibility of any evidence of ET other than that coming to us on radio waves.

Some strange sights await our closer photographic examination of Mars. In recent years an extensive investigation has been in progress which is scientific in its approach, but heretical in its subject matter. It involves close-up photographs of Mars which show, in a region called Cydonia, several pyramid-like structures accompanied by what looks like a giant human face. A monumental human face (it's a mile long) on the surface of Mars, gazing impassively towards Earth, would be a brilliant way of attracting our attention, one worthy of ET. It deserves to be real even if it isn't.

The photographic evidence provided by the original NASA photographs has been much improved by several specialists, but the evidence is still ambiguous. Yet it is good enough to make one want a closer look, even though the higher definition photography from future space flights may show unusual rock structures which don't look anything like a human face. Firstly, it's not really surprising that we can see a human face in the rocks of Mars. We're all programmed to recognise the human face. It's one of the first things a human baby has to recognise. If an inanimate object resembles a face in some vague way, we're quick to recognise that resemblance. Secondly, those rocks are several hundred million years old, at least, and the face of Homo sapiens did not appear anywhere until relatively recent times. But there is more to the story than this. The presence of unusual pyramids nearby, which are probably natural formations of considerable geological significance, makes the whole site so interesting that it is sure to receive close-up attention in the future, if for no other reason than to explore what is certainly a major mystery.

We should, therefore, review this novel but scientific investigation of the "face" and the "pyramids" – not because I think they offer evidence of ET, but because they provide the kind of phenomenon within the Solar System which one day may be inexplicable in any other way.

The Face on Mars

In July 1976, when the Lander section of Viking One had been safely landed on Mars, Orbiter One began to photograph the planet's surface. As the photographs began to arrive, a NASA scientist noticed that one frame showed a rocky structure which looked like a human face. Other scientists took a look at the photograph. The image, they decided, was produced by an unusual rock formation and the angle of the light.

The Viking Program was the major event of the time; its prime purpose was to test the top soil of Mars for evidence of life. (We now know that it was not technologically equipped to discover Martian microbes, but we will come to that subject shortly.) The Viking Program as a whole was, therefore, the overriding concern of NASA scientists when they first spotted the Face. Their attention, and that of the world's press, was focused upon other things than rocks that resembled our image on Mars. Nevertheless, newspaper correspondents were introduced to the Face at a press conference. "It's interesting," said a NASA spokesman, "but, of course, it's just a trick of the light." According to NASA at the time, no other frame had been taken which showed the face in a more revealing light, so everyone accepted that conclusion – just a pile of rocks in tricky sunlight.

Three years later, an electronics engineer named Vincent DiPietro, an image-processing specialist, saw the Face for the first time in a magazine. At the time he didn't take the magazine story seriously, but about two years later he was looking through the Viking photographs at the National Space Science Data Center in Maryland. To his surprise, he once again encountered the Face and he decided to seek more information. He found none. At this point a friend, Gregory Molenaar, a computer scientist, also became interested. The result was that they decided to do some computer image-enhancement of the photograph of the Face, known as Frame 35A72, using NASA's original tapes. (Photographic data from spacecraft is received in digital form on tape). I mention here the reference number of the frame because a second frame showing the Face was later discovered by DiPietro and Molenaar, when they searched through the Viking photographic data. It was frame 70A13 (70th orbit of Orbiter A, 13th frame). It had been taken 35 days later in a different angle of sunlight and it had been incorrectly filed.

DiPietro and Molenaar worked with the tapes and developed a new system of computer image-enhancement. Eventually, they obtained

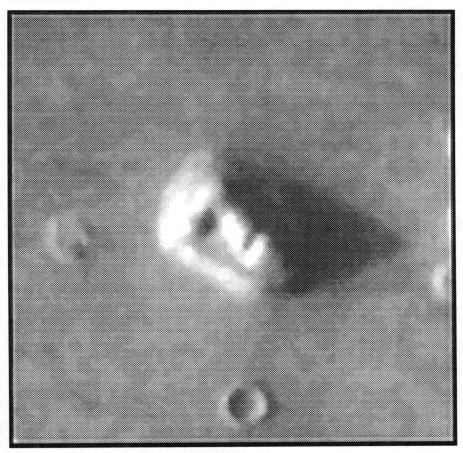

Fig. 11.1: The 'face' in the Cydonia region of Mars.

enough detail in the photographs to show, at least to their satisfaction, the symmetry of a human face (see Fig. 11.1). They then extended their research, examining photographs showing four thousand square miles of the surrounding landscape. They searched for anything which might be associated with the Face. They didn't find another face, but they did find a "pyramid", ten miles distant from the Face, measuring a mile by a mile-and-a-half (see Fig. 11.2). The previous orbiter of Mars, Mariner 9, had also photographed pyramids on Mars on the plain of Elysium, on the other side of the planet. No one thought that these had been built by Martians, but everyone was interested in this strange and unexpected geology.

Fig. 11.2: Alleged pyramids on the surface of Mars

Their research complete, as far as they thought possible with the existing data, DiPietro and Molenaar announced their findings at a meeting of the American Astronomical Society. They generated a great deal of interest for a short time. Many astronomers wanted to know all there was to know. Then things went rather quiet.

The next stage in the story involves Richard Hoagland, a science journalist who first met DiPietro and Molenaar and their research on the Face at a conference on Mars held at the University of Colorado in 1981. Hoagland had been at the NASA press conference when the photograph of the Face was first shown, and he was fascinated by what the image-enhanced photographs made by DiPietro and Molenaar seemed to show. Later, after finding other inexplicable features associated with the Face, Hoagland and several colleagues set up The Independent Mars Investigation Group which began work in December 1983. The Group thought the photographs showed things so unusual that a full investigation was needed. Numerous experts contributed to the study, including Mark Carlotto of The Analytic Sciences Corporation who carried out a three-dimensional study of the Face (see Fig. 11.1). Later Hoagland wrote a book "The Monuments of Mars", reviewing the whole subject in detail.

When I first heard about the Face, long before reading Hoagland's book, I felt that a monumental human face on Mars would be such a brilliant way to attract our attention that it deserved to be true. But in discussing evidence of erosion on the Face, Hoagland does rather undermine his hypothesis. "Such erosive features," he writes, "suggest some age to this impressive structure – under current Martian atmospheric conditions at least several million years." That's too long! Several million years ago there were no human faces for an ET sculptor to copy. To be in our image the head could be little more than a hundred thousand years old. The first Homo sapiens were not present earlier to provide a model. *Homo erectus*, our immediate ancestor, was present a million years ago, and the Face could be of *Homo erectus*, I suppose, if face it is (see Fig. 11.3). But we can hardly

Fig 11.3: *Homo erectus*, painted by Maurice Wilson. This depicts important activities which predated our technological civilisation. *Homo erectus* is believed to have been the first species to use fire.

speculate that the sculptors had enough confidence in the evolutionary future of Homo erectus to invite him to visit Mars. Go back several million years, as Hoagland suggests for the minimum age of the Face, and our closest ancestors were the Australopithecines, the ape-like creatures which populated parts of Africa at that time. The Face doesn't look like the face of an ape-man, or ape-woman.

Hoagland speculates that the builders of the City and sculptors of the Face arrived in the Solar System long ago, and they made their base on Mars because it was the only potentially habitable planet for them (if "habitable" is the right word). It was the only world near enough to the Sun with the appropriate gravity. They had crossed interstellar space from a planet smaller than Earth and, therefore, could not have borne the higher gravitational force with which we have evolved. Some astronomical theory does exist, as Hoagland points out, that Mars-like planets are far more common than Earth-like planets, but this is conjecture from incomplete data. No one really knows.

To set up home on Mars for gravitational reasons would seem a hard option for biological beings, although future human beings will surely be living and working there. Human colonies would need artificially produced gravity to stay healthy; living in a third of Earth's gravity for long periods would not suit us. But Mars is next-door for us, astronomically speaking, and might one day be used as we use Antarctica today.

Biological ETs, having crossed the light-years from another planetary system, would not be in this position. To consider one formidable problem: they would have to carry their food sources across interstellar space or synthesize everything they needed to eat. There is no food on Mars. And, being from a different biology, one based on the evolution of different kinds of proteins and biochemical processes, they wouldn't be able to use our food resources on Earth. I would thus suggest (to strengthen Hoagland's hypothesis) that his visitors to Mars were robots. They might not be greatly affected by a moderate increase or decrease in gravitational force, and they wouldn't need food – just energy. And there's no shortage of solar radiation on Mars. The scientific odds seem stacked against anyone ever meeting an alien in the Solar System, unless that alien were non-biological with no biological needs. Biological beings and interstellar space flight do not seem compatible.

Although Hoagland did speculate that biological beings arrived and established a base on Mars, I guess he would settle for non-biological beings. This point wouldn't make any difference. He is concerned with explaining the pyramids of the City and the other structures and the enormous scale of these structures, if they are more than natural rocks. Hoagland thinks that the size and complexity of the site means that the structures cannot have been built simply to send a message to Earth. He writes that, "the central problem with the *message theory* is those pyramids and their intricate connection with the Face. The sheer scale of engineering behind the construction of this massive complex argues compellingly against the message model. It is one thing to inscribe a set of geometric lines on a 20-centimeter panel of aluminum (the panels on NASA's Voyager spacecraft which tell of humans on Earth); it's quite another to array quite precisely and geometrically a set of discrete objects, some measuring kilometers across, tens of kilometers around an alien landscape – all ostensibly for the simple purpose of communicating with a remote audience ... who might never come! No, the Face by itself might be a message, but the rest of the associated features and their inextricable geometric linkage with the Face argue strongly for an indigenous reason for their presence – and all that that implies." So did ET build the Face only after civilisation evolved on Earth? It sounds like science fiction and may be science fiction – but it's testable science fiction.

Hoagland's hypothesis is barely on the edge of credibility, but he is soundly scientific. He says, "Either these features on Mars are natural and this investigation is a complete waste of time, or they are artificial and this is one of the most important discoveries of our entire existence on Earth. If they are artificial it is imperative that we figure them out, because they do not belong there."

Richard Grossinger, publisher of Hoagland's book, sums up the feelings of the investigators, "Another civilization elsewhere can have its own origin and raison d'etre without impinging on our separate terrestrial destiny, but the Face is our face, and it cannot have an exogenous or trivial explanation. If someone made it, then they picked the one object that would absolutely compel us to come there, for they have held a mirror up to our entire planet."

Hoagland's approach, thinking that he and his colleagues are on to something important, has been to head straight into a gale of criticism. As he says himself, "Science is the ultimate democracy; anyone can play, providing he or she plays by one simple rule: submitting the idea – no matter how far out – to the ultimate test: the ability of other investigators independently to arrive at the same *truth*." And the truth may soon be ours, though it might not confirm Hoagland's hypothesis. All we need are much better photographs of Mars.

We are right, of course, to be very sceptical. We have come this way before with Percival Lowell who, from his observatory in Arizona in the closing years of the last century, mapped a complex system of canals on the Martian surface, a system built, so he claimed, by an advanced civilisation to save their dying planet from terminal drought. Lowell convinced himself and half the world, though numerous astronomers opposed his views. Lowell's speculations had a great impact in his time and stimulated some great minds, including that of H. G. Wells who wrote the "War of the Worlds" as a result, which alone justified all of Lowell's shaky science.

Hoagland hasn't had that sort of effect. The world today is a more sceptical place: too many people have written books crying "Wolf" and they're still doing so. We have to allow that of all the rock formations on Mars a few are going to resemble the human face. And when we study photographs of the Martian landscape we notice that similar pyramids exist in other places, apparently one characteristic of the planet's rock formations. We have progressed from Lowell's complex system of canals to a complex of pyramids simply because this is also a case where we can't see clearly enough to identify what we're looking at. What is certain is that there are strange structures at Cydonia calling out for better photographs. We want explanations, even though no pyramid builders and sculptors may ever have set forth upon Mars.

Underlying all this is the fact that Mars is the most interesting place for SETI. We have to allow that the Solar System has been open to visits for probably the past 4 billion years, since the surfaces of the rocky planets have been solid and relatively free from meteoritic bombardment. As explained earlier, the Earth has been a shining target for any extraterrestrial s interested in life on other worlds for 350 million years, once they detected the ozone and oxygen spectral lines coming from the Sun. During the history of our planet, thousands of stars have passed relatively close to the Sun as they circled around the galactic centre. And if technological civilizations are as abundant in the Galaxy as some SETI programmes assume, then it is not impossible that evidence of past visits by advanced automated spacecraft exists somewhere within the Solar System, especially on the surfaces of the Moon and Mars.

Falsifiable Hypotheses

I am surprised at the reaction of some scientists, even those in SETI, to the work of Hoagland and his numerous talented associates. Even Frank Drake has said, "Recently, Hoagland has taken up a new cause and one that is *somewhat contrary to our purposes* (my emphasis). He has become engrossed in the so-called Face on Mars." Why should this be contrary to the purposes of SETI? Hoagland, in this particular venture, is engaged in SETI as much as any radio astronomer searching for ET's broadcasts. Actually, Hoagland's is a better scientific hypothesis than that being tested by the astronomers. Hoagland's hypothesis can be proved wrong by the next mission to Mars which provides more detailed photographs of the Cydonia region. My view is that because a positive finding would have a revolutionary impact on the human race, Hoagland is fully justified in going out on a limb in the way he has. The hypothesis that a number of advanced civilizations in the Galaxy are broadcasting signals receivable by our present astronomical technology is really a lesser scientific hypothesis because it cannot be disproved. The great philosopher of science Carl Popper has said that to be truly scientific a hypothesis has to be falsifiable. Science is not a religion. There is no one accepted truth. Science is an open house for hypotheses and their demolition, but failure to detect an intelligent signal in a thousand years would not falsify the hypothesis of astronomical SETI. Nevertheless, science must remain an open house to testable hypotheses whether they come from astronomers or scientists exploring the UFO phenomena – or monuments on Mars.

Mathematical Messages

There is one other research project involving Mars and its moon Phobos which we should consider. It has been developed mathematically and it provides a testable hypothesis. During the past 25 years, Mike Saunders, an electronics engineer who lives near London, has carried out mathematical studies in the fringe areas of SETI. He has investigated the historic sources of our fundamental units of measurement, and some of his views about possible contact with extraterrestrial intelligence in historic times have come out of this work.

Mike Saunders, thinking that the Earth might after all have been visited frequently, has looked for durable artefacts which could just possibly point to ET data banks within the Solar System. One can't rule out this possibility, and only by looking can one discover. Saunders thought that the purpose behind such an ET strategy might be that a civilization like ours could not have access to significant information until it had advanced to an appropriate level. That level might be assumed to be when a civilization was advanced enough to travel to specific points within the Solar System. Any data bank left on Earth during the past few thousand years would have been lost – or destroyed by people unaware of its significance.

So what durable stone monuments are there which might – just might – be pointers to data banks far away? Saunders' idea was that because they were built with the technology of their day they would be accepted without suspicion. He started by studying the Egyptian pyramids for any mathematical input by alien visitors at the design stage. On visiting the Great Pyramid at Gaza he was impressed by its amazing precision. Could the religious technology of Ancient Egypt, he wondered, have left a few pointers to a source of information placed somewhere in the Solar System? Several writers in the past had been puzzled by the dimensions of the Great Pyramid. It was found that its height is about one billionth the distance from the Earth to the Sun. But this is not significant. As one recent critic said, "It's like saying that the distance from London to Birmingham is 586,080 feet – precisely."

So are there mathematical values present which might be significant? The mathematical value of π (the ratio of the diameter of a circle to its circumference) was also incorporated in the Pyramid's basic measurements. Multiply the height of the Pyramid by 2π and you get its perimeter. The 52 degree slope of its sides is also the slope of a triangle having a height of 4 units of measurement and a base of π units. Yet Egyptians may not have known about the mathematical significance of π. They could have incorporated it by the use of a measuring wheel to set out the Pyramid's dimensions.

Like those before him, Saunders found other ratios that would not be considered significant by mathematicians because they are not precise enough. He found that the average distance of Mars from the Sun is about a billion times the base length of the Pyramid, but the size of the Pyramid compared to the orbit of Mars is far too small to be accepted as significant. Saunders directed his attention to the Main Chamber, the Pharaoh's burial chamber. He found that it is displaced from the centre of the Pyramid by approximately the same relative distance as Mars is displaced in its orbit around the Sun due to gravitational forces. Saunders then found that with a scaled-down orbit of Mars within the base of the Pyramid, the Pharaoh would have rested where the Sun would be in relation to Mars and the rest of the Solar System. Next he measured the access corridor to the Main Chamber, which divides the Pyramid into two unequal parts. He found here another ratio which is the same as the ratio of the Earth's year to the Martian year. So was the Pyramid a pointer to Mars, or could more be read into its measurements than was justified? Saunders continued to investigate. He drew a line from the angle of the north face of the Pyramid so that it intersected with an extended circle of the Earth's equator. The distance from the Earth to the point of intersection turned out to be the circumference of Mars.

Saunders wondered if it were possible that alien visitors to ancient Egypt might have used prominent natural phenomena to lead us one day to a contact point? He knew that NASA's spacecraft had just discovered the largest volcano in the Solar System (the Nix Olympia on Mars), so what about the largest volcano on Earth on the island of Hawaii? He found that the latitude of Hawaii is approximately 19 degrees north. He also found that Nix Olympia on Mars is 19 degrees north. The next step was to draw a line from the Pyramid through the Earth to a point 19 degrees north, and to continue that line until it intersected with the extended plane of the Earth's equator – the plane of the equator extended into space. The distance from the Earth to the point of intersection turns out to be the circumference of Mars.

Could any of these findings lead anywhere? Saunders then had a good idea. The surface of Mars is frequently whipped by fierce winds which propel sand around the planet. Any ET data bank there would have to be shielded in some way, but Mars has two tiny moons, Deimos and Phobos, which are totally free from erosion. Could one of these be a contact point? He drew a line from the orbit of Deimos to latitude 19 degrees north on the Martian surface, and then continued the line through to the other side of the planet where it comes out at latitude $25\frac{1}{4}$ degrees north. From that point on the planet's surface, an identical structure to the Great Pyramid would point to Phobos, the second moon of Mars.

Now to the final destination of Saunders' mathematical journey. He drew a line through the slope of what would be the Great Pyramid on Mars, situated at $25\frac{1}{4}$ degrees north, to the centre of Phobos. The line meets the moon at latitude 12.88 degrees north. He then drew a line from the centre of the Pyramid on Mars to the centre of Phobos, when Phobos is directly overhead. This line meets the moon at a longitude of 0 degrees. Saunders concluded from this that a target site might exist on Phobos at a latitude of 12.88 degrees on longitude 0 degrees. "The site would be within an error of about 10 metres." He points out the uniqueness of Phobos. "It is the only moon in the Solar System which orbits faster than the rotation of its parent planet on its axis. I find the mathematical relationships between the Great Pyramid, the largest volcanoes on Mars and on the Earth, Phobos and Deimos – and the fact that Mars has only two moons – all a bit too remarkable to be put down to coincidence. But I'm always willing to be proved wrong."

The only test would be to go to Phobos, which future missions will do. Phobos will make an excellent space station for future explorations of Mars, and the moons of Mars themselves will have to be explored. They are a strange couple, looking like cratered rugby balls. Their orbits around the Martian equator are nearly circular, which needs an explanation. If they were asteroids captured by the gravitational field of Mars, such order would be unexpected. But their orbits are not stable. Mars is pulling on Phobos, which will crash onto the planet within the next 100 million years – a short period in the life expectancy of moons. Deimos will move the other way, drifting outwards, eventually to be lost.

Checking the detailed work that Saunders has done over many years would not be easy. It would almost be easier to go to Phobos and test the hypothesis. Saunders himself would be the first to admit that he may have formed his hypothesis by unintentionally discovering the mathematical relationships which favour it. Yet he thinks a look at the specified site on Phobos would be justified. When astronauts land there in the next century they would not be far away. With the site precisely marked, this subject is rather like a combination of "Star Trek" and "Treasure Island".

Chapter Twelve

SETI and the
Human Situation

ertrand Russell once said that what made today so different
from yesterday was science and technology; that no other
influence on our lives has had much effect by comparison.
From what we see around us this is clearly so. The landscape abounds
– we can often say is littered – with the products of technology,
flowing from the advance of science. Less obviously, our attitudes
and ideas have also been changed by the same scientific advance.
Inside our heads we are as different from the past as is our present
technological environment. It is this unseen change, which new
knowledge brings, that directs the way society will go and makes
forecasting the future such a leap into the unknown.

This aspect of tomorrow is rarely explored in Science fiction films
on television. Take the brand leader "Star Trek". The crews of the
starship 'Enterprise' (both the old one and the new one) have ideas,
beliefs, attitudes, and patterns of behaviour which characterise the
best in present-day America. We can't complain about this in a space
saga which often uses science fiction to deal with present-day problems, but the attitudes and ideas that dominate in the 23rd Century
will surely be different from those of today.

Clearly, we can't anticipate what these differences will be in just a
few centuries time. What chance do we have, therefore, of guessing
the attitudes of intelligent non-humans who could be hundreds of
thousands of years ahead of us? We've already seen that we cannot
expect to find ETs of a lower technological status than ourselves.
Contact with beings thousands of years ahead of ourselves could
consequently involve contact with minds even more difficult to
understand than their technology. Any successful attempt to under-

stand either would change our civilization, either quickly or slowly, slightly or entirely, depending on the type of contact.

The impact of a data bank describing an entire alien civilization, left, say, on the Moon, might be greater than a message from a distant star. In either case, the ET information would only be slowly unravelled and understood. Society might absorb it over a long period of time and avoid serious damage in the process. The greatest shock for society would be definite confirmation that a few of those thousands of reported UFOs are alien spacecraft. To those not familiar with the science involved in SETI, this might look more dangerous than the grand combination of nuclear arms, energy shortages, over-population, dwindling resources and pollution. My conclusion, from what we've learned through exploring the rationale for astronomical SETI, is that there would be no need to worry. Since we appreciate the dangers of contact with less advanced societies, so too would the ETs. Avoidance of direct contact with emerging world civilizations, such as ours, would be the "prime directive", to use the "Star Trek" jargon. We have speculated that planets like Earth are protected, and no more than vague signs of an ET presence in the universe will ever be found during our present stage of development.

Society would not, therefore, be changed, except mentally. Indisputable evidence of alien beings beyond our boundaries might act as a catalyst, awakening our awareness of the human situation. People everywhere, for the first time, would see themselves as one species. Whereas religions and politics divide us, an ET presence could unite us, even though any direct contact would seem to be highly unlikely.

ET will get you if you Don't Watch Out

Some would fear even an ET signal from across the Galaxy. "If the cosmic telephone rings, for God's sake let us not answer," said Professor Zolenek Topal some 25 years ago. Early in 1996, after confirmation that three planets had been detected in orbit about three neighbouring stars like the Sun, Professor Robert Rood, of Harvard University, said much the same thing. "The civilization that blurts out its existence on interstellar beacons at the first opportunity may be like some early hominid descending from the trees and calling, 'Here, kitty,' to a sabre-toothed tiger."

I believe this line of thinking completely ignores the reality of our situation. If advanced ETs are out there, then the evolution of life and technological intelligence must be part of the universal process. They won't be out there if this is not so. If they are out there in our epoch, broadcasting across the Galaxy, they must have been doing so since the evolution of the first technological civilizations took place a few billion years ago. For statistical reasons they cannot otherwise be present in our epoch, and Frank Drake and his many brilliant colleagues stand no chance at all of detecting call signals or messages. It follows from this that if ETs are out there, ready to pounce on us, as Robert Rood suggests, and near enough to detect any interstellar beacon which we might transmit, then they would be near enough to have long ago detected the presence of Earth as a life-supporting planet. The reader will have seen earlier that, in theory, ET could have detected the presence of life on this planet at any time during the past 350 million years, since the presence of the Earth's oxygen atmosphere became detectable, mainly by the prominent ozone line from our ozone layer. A capability in astronomy a mere hundred years in advance of what we currently possess would have been enough for this detective work. We can already see how it could be done and are planning to do it ourselves. We could start to develop the necessary technology today, given the economic resources.

So did enthusiastic ETs begin to transmit their signals and messages towards the Solar System 350 million years ago when the evolving amphibians on Earth, just emerging from the swamps, were rather short of radio receivers? Have the alien astronomers of many different worlds transmitted their broadcasts to the radio-deaf ears of pre-technological life after detecting an oxygen atmosphere in the Solar System? We know the sort of time period it takes for life to produce radio receivers and so would advanced ETs. Therefore, because of the very high improbability of radio receivers being present, the ETs would send space probes across the light-years to explore, if this level of space technology was available. If interstellar space flight can't be developed for some reason, then those warnings to us not to reply to interstellar beacons do not apply. If other world civilizations have been near enough at times in the past few billion years, and have had the appropriate space technology, then they would have visited the Solar System. But if ETs are rare and widely separated within the Galaxy, making interstellar travel not a feasible option, then communications between worlds can only be carried out by radio or light or some similar means not yet discovered by us. So whether the ETs of the Galaxy have detected our radio transmissions or not makes no difference. The warnings of Zolenek Topal and Robert Rood have no basis, and there is no reason for ETs to come here now rather than at any other time. If you were an ET wanting to take over a planet – the old science fiction plot – you would not choose a planet covered by intelligent civilization. If ET wanted to take over the Earth, an unattractive task because of all the biological problems, he could have done so more easily before civilization emerged, when there were only dumb animals to deal with.

Permanent Signals

What would be our reaction if we detected an ET signal today? Some would welcome the signal with enthusiasm as a turning point in human history. We all would sense a power beyond ourselves, and an outside power has always made us one with our neighbours. We might even respond to the Einstein-Russell appeal, made shortly before Einstein's death, to "remember that you belong to the human race and forget the rest".

Perhaps we are still somewhat like our ancestors, the half-human apes of the African savannahs of a few million years ago, who huddled together in the chill of night watching the stars overhead. We gaze in awe at the stars, where city lights don't dim the spectacle, but we want to know if there are other planets out there orbiting those stars, planets with unimaginable lifeforms and civilizations beyond our understanding. Yet we know that it is just possible that we are living on the only inhabited world in the Galaxy, and we don't want to be the most unlikely accident in time and space. So are inhabited worlds abundant or very rare, or somewhere between these two extremes? SETI is the only way to find answers.

Professor Paul Davies, who writes so splendidly about physics, thinks that the widespread interest in SETI is motivated by our religious feelings. "The interest in SETI among the general public stems in part, I maintain, from the need to find a wider context for our lives than this earthly existence provides." He believes this also applies to the scientists involved. "This sense of a religious quest may well extend to the scientists themselves ..."

One could say this about many areas of science. Prominent physicists proclaim their ambition to "know the mind of God". And mathematical physicists search for "the Holy Grail" in their endeavours to discover the grand theory which unites all the forces in nature. Some years ago I noted a quotation from Giordano Bruno, who was burnt at the stake in Rome in 1660 for promoting the wicked belief in the plurality of inhabited worlds. He said, "There is one basic cause of all effects." Theoretical physicists throughout the world are today trying to prove him right.

Biologists don't talk quite so much about God as the physicists and cosmologists, but there is a religious element in wanting to know if all life on Earth is a unique accident or an inevitable part of the grand process. It is a captivating puzzle which we would all like to solve, whether or not we hold any particular religious beliefs.

The Meaning for Us

Failure to discover evidence of ETs after a long search could indicate that we are the beneficiaries of some unlikely events. For example, the evolution of large brains capable of developing technology may hardly ever be selected for in nature because of the high energy requirements of large brains. The odds against the evolution of a technological species might be too great for such an event to occur more than once in an epoch (of perhaps a hundred million years) in the history of a galaxy.

We can view the past and our possible future, from the origin of life to the exploration of the nearest stars with planetary systems, and we can see that the absence of just one stage of the journey makes the complete journey impossible. Yet we have already completed part of the journey, whether it be by chance or by some inevitable unfolding of a universal process. Can anything now stop us reaching the stars? It could be impossible. Interstellar space could harbour obstacles we have yet to discover. If it proves to be impossible in our future even after we have developed the ultimate in space propulsion it would have been impossible for other species in the past, and the only means of contact would be by astronomical SETI.

Which of the alternative scenarios which we have considered would we choose to be true? Perhaps the most acceptable for us would be that all technological beings eventually meet a low technological ceiling, because there are no more fundamental aspects of nature to discover and apply. Even with a high technological ceiling, all flights to the stars (for the biological reasons considered earlier) may be made by non-biological entities and automatic spacecraft. One cannot imagine highly intelligent beings spending their lives crossing the light-years to study other planetary systems, when their technology would make it possible for hard-wearing and hard-working robots to do the job for them.

Alternatively, it seems to me that if technology has a high ceiling, or none at all (though this seems impossible in a finite universe), then by now the Galaxy should be thoroughly explored. If the ceiling is low, then many technological civilizations may go into space and explore and colonize their own planetary systems, yet not go on to the stars, except for sending intelligent probes.

Therefore, if interstellar travel can become a routine activity we would be in an 'all situation': that is, an explored and documented Galaxy – planet Earth might even appear on someone's charts. Otherwise, in view of current scientific information, ETs may be rare and widely separated because the planets on which they could evolve are rare and widely separated, and because we can now see why it has taken about 3½ billion years on Earth to move from micro-organisms to a technological lifeform. The important evidence which supports this conclusion consists of those fossils of photosynthesizing bacteria which have been dated at 3½ billion years old (see fig 4:5). We can see various periods in the history of life, from microbes to technologists, which may have been longer or shorter on other worlds, but our best guess is that it has probably taken a similar length of time for other civilized beings to evolve. We can also see why on a proportion of Earth-like planets no technological species may ever evolve, though such planets may support an abundance of life.

Where is ET?

Why is there no obvious sign of ET's past or present activities in the Solar System? The asteroids, an attractive source of building materials for space colonies, exist for our future space projects. The surface of the Moon looks as virginal as the driven snow, although astronauts have explored only tiny regions of that world. We can't yet say the same about Mars, and, as we have seen in Chapter Eleven, we need photography of greater resolving power before we can definitely dismiss the hypothesis put forward by Richard Hoagland and his colleagues. Even if the new photography shows that the famous "Face and City" are just piles of rocks, we cannot rule out past explorations of the planet, and we won't easily be able to do so. Whatever our gut feeling about this, we could not be certain until a vast amount of exploration has been carried out. It may take centuries to reach a scientifically justifiable negative conclusion.

It could be that we haven't noticed anything (except some inexplicable UFO phenomena) because everything has been left more or less undisturbed by ETs from various periods in galactic history. The Solar System with its single blue planet may be valued for its rarity. The ETs would know, from their own experiences, that new technological species can survive and advance only by migrating into space, so they would leave the Solar System for us. As the late Gerard O'Neill has pointed out, the resources within the Solar System should allow the continued growth of our civilization for the next 5,000 years. Enough time perhaps to develop social and political stability, and the science and technology to move on to the stars, if that is possible. Without this option, our civilization might soon be doomed to extinction. There has to be an outlet for a species so locked into development and expansion.

The Persistent Question

After giving such a speculative assessment of the possible situation out there, one is often still questioned by people who expect clearly observable evidence of ET activity, if extraterrestrial s have ever visited the Solar System. They somehow believe that we should be able to detect such evidence, if it exists. Unfortunately or fortunately, depending on your point of view, we are far from such a capability.

One way to look at the problem is to imagine ourselves outside the Galaxy, trying to guess the answer. Imagine we know everything that we do at present except one thing – just one item of information is withheld from us. We do not know if human beings have detected evidence of past or present ET activity within the Solar System or among our neighbourhood stars. Would we therefore conclude that the Solar System has never been visited during the past few billion years, the sort of period during which advanced technology and interstellar travel could be possible, if the scientific rationale for astronomical SETI is correct? Or, alternatively, would we conclude that there have been no visits because there has been no one out there capable of making such visits? I think we would conclude it more probable that ETs have visited the Solar System.

Now, while we are still outside the Galaxy and guessing, let us be given the information that human beings have not detected evidence of any extraterrestrial intelligence. Would this additional piece of information change our first conclusion? Would we think that this information indicated that the Galaxy has not, after all, been explored during the past few billion years, or would we think that human beings, after a few decades of science, of space technology and astronomy, have not yet had enough time to discover the evidence? I believe that most of us would back the second alternative: that evidence is there but that we haven't yet discovered it, rather than that it is not there at all.

Of course, there may be some essential item of information missing from the ET debate which would greatly enhance our understanding. I remember three astronomers being interviewed on television many years ago about the origin of the universe. At that time, astronomers were about equally divided in their support for the 'big bang' and 'steady state' theories of the universe. There wasn't at that time the observational evidence to reach a decision one way or the other. One astronomer supported one theory; one supported the other, and there was an enthusiastic discussion about which was correct. After a while, the interviewer turned to the third astronomer who had been listening quietly. Which theory, the interviewer asked, did he think was correct? "The one we haven't thought of yet," he replied. Instantly, our intellectual feet touched solid ground. Judging by the history of science, the third astronomer has the best chance of being right. And so it may be with us. The answer to Fermi's question, "Where is everybody?" could be the one we haven't thought of yet. If you think of it, patient reader, do write and let me know.

Appendix 1

References and Recommended Books

Baird, J.C., 'The Inner Limits of Outer Space', University Press of New England, 1987. A review of SETI by a Professor of Psychology who considers the human factors which motivate the searchers and questions the validity of some assumptions.

Billingham, J., 'Life in the Universe', the MIT Press, 1979. An extensive collection of papers (some technical) given at the 'Life in the Universe' conference held by NASA in 1979.

Bounias, Prof. Michael C.L., 'Biochemical Traumatology as a Potent Tool for Plant Metabolic Disorders in Correlation with a UFO Landing', Journal of Scientific Exploration, vol. 4, no. 1, pp 1-18, 1990.

Bracewell, R.N., 'The Galactic Club', W.H. Freeman and Company, 1975.

Drake, F. & Sobel, D., 'Is Anyone Out There?', Delacorte Press, New York, 1992. A first-hand account of the history of observational SETI by the radio astronomer who carried out the first search. Besides the history, it contains much interesting material on the astronomical problems of SETI.

'First Contact', a collection of authoritative and readable essays on various aspects of SETI by leading scientists in the subject. Published 1990, in paperback, by Headline Book Publishing.

Goldsmith , D. and Owen, T., 'The Search for Life in the Universe', Benjamin/Cummings, California, 1980, Second Edition. Scientifically comprehensive and extensively illustrated.

Hoagland, Richard C., 'The Monuments of Mars', North Atlantic

Books, 1987. A comprehensive account of how the data on two NASA photographs led to the development of the hypothesis that ruined buildings and a monument of a human face exist on Mars.

Horowitz, N.H., 'To Utopia and Back' 'The Search for Life in the Solar System', W.H. Freeman and Company, 1986. An examination of the prospects for life elsewhere in the Solar System by one of the scientists who has been leading NASA's investigations.

Kingsley, Dr. Stuart (ed), 'The Search for Extraterrestrial Intelligence (SETI) in the Optical Spectrum' proceedings of International Society for Optical Engineering, vol. 1867, 1993. The first comprehensive review of this developing branch of SETI. Contact for optical SETI: Dr Stuart Kingsley, Columbus Optical SETI Observatory, 545 Northview Drive, Columbus, OH 43209-1051, USA.

McDonough, T.R., 'The Search for Extraterrestrial Intelligence Listening for Life in the Cosmos', John Wiley & Sons, New York, 1987. Extensively illustrated.

Morrison, Philip, et al. (eds), 'The Search for Extraterrestrial Intelligence, published by NASA, 1977. Reports the findings of the SETI workshops held at the Ames Research Center, California. Technical.

O'Neill, G.K., 'The High Frontier', William Morrow of New York and Corgi Books. A book on the colonization of space by the scientist who showed that space colonies were no longer confined to science fiction. A detailed but non-technical treatment of the subject.

Papagiannis, M.D. (ed), 'The Search for Extraterrestrial Life: Recent Developments', D. Reidel Publishing Company, 1985. The proceedings of the symposium held at Boston University in 1984. A large collection of papers, some rather technical, on many aspects of SETI.

Rather, John D.G., 'Lasers Revisited: their superior utility for interstellar beacons, communications and travel', Journal of The British Interplanetary Society, vol. 44, pp 385-392, 1991.

Regis, E.Jr. (ed), 'Extraterrestrial s Science and Alien Intelligence', Cambridge University Press, 1985. A collection of original and reprinted articles.

Ridpath, I., 'Messages from the Stars', Fontana Books and Harper & Row of New York, 1978.

Sagan, C. (ed), 'Communication with Extraterrestrial Intelligence', The MIT Press, Massachusetts. A collection of papers given at the symposium at the Byurakan Astrophysical Observatory, USSR, in 1972.

Sagan, C., 'Cosmos', Random House and Futura, 1980. The Book of the television series by the same name. Deals with studies of life and the universe which everyone interested in SETI must consider.

Tipler, Frank. References to all Frank Tipler's SETI papers are given here because of their importance to the SETI debate: "Extraterrestrial Intelligent Beings do not Exist", Quarterly Journal of the Royal Astronomical Society, 1980, vol. 21, pp. 267-281; "A Brief History of the Extraterrestrial Intelligence Concept", Quarterly Journal of the Royal Astronomical Society, 1981, vol. 22, pp. 133-145; "Additional Remarks on Extraterrestrial Intelligence", Quarterly Journal of the Royal Astronomical Society, 1981, vol. 22, pp. 279-292; "The Most Advanced Civilization in the Galaxy Is Ours", Mercury, January-February 1982, pp. 5-37; "Extraterrestrial Intelligence: the debate continues" (a comprehensive review paper with several contributors), Physics Today, March 1982, pp. 27-38.

Velasco, Dr. J.J., 'Scientific Approach and First Results of Studies into Unidentified Aerospace Phenomena in France', presented at AIAA Conference, Los Angeles, April 19, 1986.

Astronomers (advanced amateurs and professionals) interested in investigating the Astronautical Theory should write to Roy Dutton, c/o 545 Babbacombe Road, Torquay, Devon TQ1 1HQ

'Mars Underground New', readable and authoritative, a quarterly news letter, published by the Planetary Society, 65 North Catalina Avenue, Pasadena, California 91106-2301.

'Search for Past Life on Mars: Possible Relic Biogenic Activity in Martian Meteoite ALH84001', a technical research article by the researchers who claimed the discovery of the Martian microbes, Science, vol. 273, August 16, 1996.

'Destiny Mars' by M.W. Saunders, published 1975, Chaldon Press, Caterham, Surrey, provides the mathematical details of Saunders' hypothesis.

Appendix 2

Associations which promote SETI and related space research

British Interplanetary Society, 27/29 South Lambeth Road, London, SW8 1SZ. Has a long-established reputation for the promotion of astronautics and related subjects. Publishes a monthly magazine and a quarterly technical journal. Both these publications sometimes deal with SETI and related subjects.

The Planetary Society, 65 N. Catalina Avenue, Pasadena, CA 91106. Actively supports SETI and the exploration of the Solar System. Has over one hundred thousand members worldwide. It publishes an illustrated magazine, 'The Planetary Report', six times a year.

SETI Institute, 101 First Street, # 410, Los Altos, California 94022. Formed in 1984, it 'promotes research and related activities regarding the search for extraterrestrial life, particularly intelligent life...'. It now runs Project Phoenix, which was NASA's SETI Program until government support was withdrawn. It publishes an excellent quarterly news report 'SETI News'.

'SETI Quest', an authoritative quarterly magazine on SETI and bio-astronomy, published by Helmers Publishing, Inc., 174 Concord Street, Peterborough, N. H. 03458-0874, USA.

Space Studies Institute, P.O. Box 82, Princeton, New Jersey 08540. Established by Gerard O'Neill who first showed the technical feasibility of space colonies. Supports research projects associated with the technology of space colonization, and publishes its own journal.

Index